# INTERIOR BALLISTICS

EDWARD D. LOWRY, a graduate of the University of Illinois, is Director of Fundamental Research for Winchester-Western Division of Olin Mathieson Chemical Corporation. Mr. Lowry is the author of *Exterior Ballistics of Small Arms Projectiles* as well as a number of articles in *Weapons Technology, The American Rifleman,* and other publications.

The Chemistry in Action Series has been designed to give the interested layman a thorough introduction to the many different sides of the chemical industry. Prepared under the joint supervision of the Education Activities Committee of the Manufacturing Chemists' Association and Doubleday & Company, Inc., each volume focuses on a particular segment of the chemical industry and relates the pure chemical science to the final products met in everyday life. The volumes have each been written by distinguished authorities in the field, and cover such various fields as agricultural chemistry, chemicals from the atmosphere and from the ocean, and the chemistry of paints, the soil, water purification, sulfuric acid, the silicon compounds, synthetic textiles, drugs, and antibiotics.

# INTERIOR BALLISTICS

*How a Gun Converts Chemical Energy into Projectile Motion*

### E. D. LOWRY

PREPARED UNDER THE SPONSORSHIP OF
THE MANUFACTURING CHEMISTS' ASSOCIATION, INC.

Anchor Books
Doubleday & Company, Inc.
Garden City, New York

*Interior Ballistics* was published simultaneously
in a hardcover edition by Doubleday & Company, Inc.

Anchor Books edition: 1968

# CONTENTS

# CONTENTS

# INTRODUCTION

Many of us, at one time or another, have enjoyed firing a gun. It may have been during the excitement of deer hunting in the northern woodlands, or while pleasantly testing our skill at breaking fast-moving clay targets, or perhaps while indulging in the lazy pastime of plinking away at old bottles and tin cans. But whatever the game, it always appears as if the acts of firing the gun and of hitting the target are virtually simultaneous. Actually the time interval from the instant the trigger is squeezed until the projectile crashes into a nearby target is less than the time it takes to blink an eye. Yet, in that brief fraction of a second, a large number of complex phenomena have all taken place. For convenience, the study of these various phenomena is known collectively as ballistics, the science of the movement of projectiles. This term, however, has become a little too general, and so ballistics is now broken down into three distinct and separate technologies: interior ballistics, which is concerned with what takes place inside the barrel; exterior ballistics, which is concerned with the aerodynamic forces acting on the projectile during its flight; and terminal ballistics, which is concerned with the dynamics of target impact. We will be concerned only with the first of these.

Interior ballistics is a science which explores the manner by which the chemical energy, stored in a propellant, is released and converted to the kinetic energy of a projectile. For easy visualization, we can think of this process of energy conversion as taking place in three stages.

In the first stage, the propellant decomposes into gaseous products and, at the same time, releases an enormous amount of heat. These are chemical phenomena. In the second stage, during decomposition of the propellant, its chemical energy is being converted into heat which is then contained in the confined gases. This causes high pressures in the gun and on the projectile that accelerate it and give it motion. Thus, the energy in the form of heat is in turn converted into the kinetic energy of the projectile. These are all thermodynamic phenomena. Finally, in the third stage, the pressures act on the projectile to accelerate it forward while overcoming friction; they induce stresses in the barrel and also cause the gun to recoil. These are all physical phenomena. It is thus apparent that interior ballistics is based on a foundation of chemistry, thermodynamics, and physics.

The primary purpose of this book is to illustrate the fundamental principles upon which interior ballistics is based. Our approach to the subject matter will be to first examine individually the three processes—chemical, thermodynamic, and physical—which take place inside a gun. In each one, there are basic principles that underlie the nature of the process. For example, the thermodynamic principle of the conversion of energy simply states that the total amount of energy in the system is constant. While the propellant is burning, there is *chemical* energy stored in the fraction of unburned propellant; there is *heat* energy in the hot gases and *kinetic* energy in the projectile; and energy has also been used to heat the barrel, to overcome friction, and to spin the projectile. The distribution of energy in these various forms changes very rapidly, but the total quantity of energy remains unchanged. After a consideration of the underlying principles and a scrutinizing of each of the three processes, it will then be possible to tie them together and obtain some insight into the interior ballistic phenomena that take place inside a gun. Finally, this will all help show how such parameters as propellant composition, grain geometry, and many others influence the two predominantly important characteristics of any gun system: the peak pressure in the gun tube and the muzzle velocity of the projectile.

An adequate comprehension of any subject matter requires not only a firm grasp of the fundamental principles, but an appreciation of the important quantitative magnitudes as well. For instance, we already know a little about the interior ballistics in a shotgun once we know that a 10,000 psi peak pressure in the barrel is reached when the $1\frac{1}{8}$ ounces of shot have traveled about two inches down the bore, that the muzzle velocity is 1250 feet per second, that the total time from propellant ignition to muzzle exit is .003 second, and that this is all made to happen by .018 ounce of propellant. A quantitative magnitude, however, implies some method for its measurement. In interior ballistics, being as it is an experimental science, the principal tools have included methods for measuring the important quantities. Accordingly, a secondary purpose of this book is to describe the various experimental techniques used for measuring interior ballistic quantities and to then give the characteristic magnitude of these quantities in typical gun systems.

Interior ballistics is not strictly within the province of guns; it applies to any system where a propellant is used to give motion to a body such as a projectile or a rocket. Although gun systems are used throughout this book because of their convenience in helping to describe the fundamentals of interior ballistics, coverage of the subject cannot be complete without a brief consideration of other interior ballistics systems. Accordingly, one chapter is devoted specifically to the interior ballistics of rockets.

# INTERIOR BALLISTICS

# CHAPTER 1

# HISTORICAL BACKGROUND

Primitive man spent most of his existence in an uncertain struggle for sustenance and survival. The unending quest for food and a continuous need to defend himself led to frequent, often sudden, and always dangerous encounters with the beasts that shared his wild environment. Too often, in these unavoidable close-quarter combats, his rude club or spear was not enough to overcome the advantages of a stronger, fleeter, more savage adversary. His ability to endure and survive against such odds was always questionable. However, he managed to change this precarious balance with his first great technological feat, the development of the bow. Now he had a real weapon. With this device, at a safe distance from his target, he could slowly store muscular energy into the bow, hold it briefly, and release it suddenly for accurate delivery to his target. The bow thus became a big first step in man's mastery of his environment, for with it he could now successfully hunt the swiftest game, overcome the fiercest animals, or protect himself against antagonistic neighbors.

For fifty thousand years the bow remained man's most effective hand weapon. But even though improved and made more efficient over the centuries, the bow suffered from a limiting disadvantage. It could not deliver any more energy to an arrow than a man, by his own strength, could store into the bow. Inevitably it was made virtually obsolete by another revolutionary development—gunpowder. The discovery of gunpowder became a great early step in man's learning to unlock the many doors to reservoirs of energy that nature had disguised in other forms. The development of gunpowder, nevertheless, was very slow as revolutions go and actually covered hundreds of years. Historically, the sequence from the early crude black powders to the powerful propellants of today can be broken down into two phases: the development of black powder, which started in the Middle Ages and took several centuries; and the development of modern propellants, which was begun late in the last century with smokeless powder.

During the long first phase, there was no such thing as a science of interior ballistics. Accordingly, progress in perfecting gunpowder and its uses was very slow, since no one really had more than a crude comprehension of the basic nature of a gun system. Improvements were therefore the very slow results of trial and often fatal error. In fact, it was not until a few decades ago that interior ballistics graduated from a vague art to a science. Finally, it was this fundamental understanding of the complex interior ballistics phenomena that accelerated the development of today's ballistics systems—from the sleek, high-powered rifle of the hunter to the rocket systems that make possible travel beyond our planet.

## THE HISTORY OF BLACK POWDER

Before we begin our story of black powder, it might be helpful if we first identify it by giving a brief description of its composition and its performance characteristics. Black powder is a deceptively simple mixture of three easily obtainable ingredients: charcoal, sulfur, and potassium nitrate, or saltpeter. In its long history of development, various proportions have been tried, but the optimum performance is obtained with about 10 per cent sulfur, 15 per cent charcoal, and 75 per cent potassium nitrate. These are individually ground to a powder, mechanically mixed, ground together, and then incorporated with the help of moisture and pressure into hard cakes, which are dried and broken down into the desired granulation. In this mixture, the charcoal (which is predominantly carbon) is the fuel, and the saltpeter is the oxygen supplier or oxidizer. Sulfur helps to make the mixture more readily ignitable and helps give it more density and workability. When black powder is burned properly in a gun, it will produce 44 per cent of its original weight in hot gases and 56 per cent in solid residues, which appear principally as a dense white smoke. One pound of good black powder contains, as stored chemical energy, the equivalent of 600,000 foot-pounds, of which roughly one-third can be converted to the kinetic energy of a projectile in a reasonably efficient gun system.

Nobody really knows who first discovered the violent burning characteristics of this mixture of sulfur, charcoal, and potassium nitrate. On the basis of various vague and ambiguous ancient writings, one could be led to believe that black powder was first used by the Chinese many centuries ago, or by the Arabs, who allegedly employed it at the siege of Mecca in A.D. 690, or even that it was one of the many secrets imputed to the ancient Hindus. Although various forms of this mixture may have been known to all these people, the early reliable references appear in Europe during the Middle Ages. The first identifiable individuals who come upon the scene in the shadowy early history are three monks. The first of these is Marcus Graecus, a Greek, whose manuscript *Liber Ignium* describes an explosive compound of one part sulfur, two parts charcoal, and six parts saltpeter, which, it says, is excellent for "making thunder." This work, presently located in the National Library of Paris, is dated A.D. 848, and is the first identifiable reference to specifically list the three ingredients of black powder. Nevertheless, there are those skeptics who believe this material on black powder may have been added in the thirteenth century. The second monk is an Englishman, Friar Roger Bacon, who in 1248 mysteriously concealed a description of the ingredients in an anagram. Many historians feel that this is the first authenticated description of black powder. Finally, a German monk from Freiburg, Berthold the Black, is identified not only with the discovery of black powder, but with the invention of the gun sometime roughly in the late thirteenth or early fourteenth century. In any event, black powder was certainly known by the thirteenth century and may have been used as a noisy and flashy pyrotechnic long before this time. However, its earliest use as a propellant to fire a projectile from a gun has been recorded as early as 1313. Henceforth, "this powder used for guns" was more commonly known as "gunpowder."

There is an old Chinese custom for starting the day by lighting a firecracker to frighten away the unfriendly spirits. In the days of its earliest uses, black powder was probably more effective in frightening a foe with noise, flash, and smoke than in actually causing sensible, physical damage. Subsequently, it was employed to tip fire arrows and then as an explosive. A sufficient quantity of powder, for example, if judiciously placed underneath a defensive wall, could tear a hole big enough to provide entry to the attacking forces. Finally men learned that the directed energy could be much more deadly and effective, and so the gun was invented. The first guns were crude affairs and the first projectiles were probably made of easily available stone. The metal tube was called a "barrel" simply because it was made like a barrel and its construction consisted of a number of iron bars bound together with iron hoops, since this was much easier in fabrication than the more sophisticated and time-consuming art of casting metal. The earliest guns were used for firing large projectiles, but these were shortly followed by a smaller handgun that could be carried and discharged by a single individual. These early handguns were extremely crude affairs, consisting of a simple iron tube, closed at one end and held by means of a pole. The fire could be applied to the propellant charge through a drilled hole, as illustrated in Figure 1. This was hardly a very effective weapon, and the amount of damage the gunner could inflict was at best questionable. To begin, he poured an uncertain amount of crude gunpowder down a barrel; he then added stones, pieces of metal, or other debris, and finally used a piece of cloth or a wad of grass to ram home these projectiles and hold them in place. Aiming was difficult, since the man's attention was too much concerned with getting his charge ignited. His device was cumbersome and inaccurate, and outside of the noise, flash, and smoke it produced, was hardly more lethal to an enemy than to himself.

These crude handguns were very probably first used in the late fourteenth or early fifteenth century. Ineffective as they were, these handguns and the awkward boulder-throwing cannons of the time marked the beginnings of a revolutionary new technology of warfare. Yet for the next few centuries the multitude of secret formulas for manufacturing black powder, and the completely unscientific approach to improving gun performance, made the foundations of ballistics more a superstition than an art. This superstition that grew up around the use of gunpowder took some bizarre forms. Because of its explosive powers, it was variously believed to have other wonderful properties. Huntsmen would often sprinkle gunpowder on their cooked meat for seasoning. It was once believed by some that moderate doses would give a man power and courage. The smoke of burning gunpowder was even considered to have disinfectant properties, and orders were allegedly given at Valley Forge

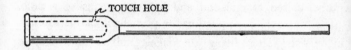
TOUCH HOLE

Fig. 1. Earliest handgun.

to "have the powder of a Musket Cartridge burnt in each Hutt dayly to purify the Air . . ."

One very unpleasant difficulty with black powder was its unpredictable habit of exploding at the wrong time. In its manufacture, the most dangerous operation was always the grinding or "milling" of the powder. Here the ingredients, after being thoroughly mixed and sifted, were ground in special stone or iron mills. To obtain a sufficiently fine mixture, this milling process required several hours. There was always a danger of explosion, since the material could be easily touched off by a static spark. During the early days of its manufacture, the explosions were so frequent that work at a manufacturing establishment was extremely hazardous. Even as its manufacture became more standardized and certain necessary precautions were systematically followed, the dangers were still considerable. In fact, according to one description of typical powder mill operation in this country, the practice was to build a stout skeleton framework of beams with a good strong roof and a flock of decrepit boards loosely tacked on the sides. The workmen mixed the batches, prepared them for the milling operation, started up the operation, and then left the building. These precautions lessened the danger to the workmen, but the frequency of "blows" underscored the ever-present unpredictable hazard of manufacturing gunpowder. Even today the dangers exist too often for the schoolboy who is lured by the easy formula and simple process for making up a batch of black powder. A failure to appreciate the essential precautions still leads to severe burns and worse to many young experimenters in countless basements and back sheds.

The dangers were not all in the manufacture of gunpowder. Again the imperfect knowledge of a gun's strength and an injudicious overcharge of powder during the heat of battle often resulted in a blown gun and a dead gunner. In fact, one of the early problems in the use of guns was to make guns safer to friends as well as more fatal to enemies. When firing the early crude artillery pieces, the hazards were so well known that the unfortunate gunners were often chosen from condemned criminals and were chained to their posts. Another unpleasant hazard grew out of the fact that gunpowder, since it was a simple mixture of ingredients, would not remain homogeneous, and as a result of too much joggling over the rough roads of the time, the sulfur would settle to the bottom and the powder would become ineffective. One way to obviate this difficulty was by carrying the three ingredients in separate containers to the place of use and then the ingredients would be mixed on the spot just prior to use. Needless to say, the act of mixing was the last earthly act of many an unfortunate cannoneer's helper.

Little improvement was made over Friar Bacon's old formula until the sixteenth century. The gunners of the time were hampered by the nature of gunpowder, which was truly a powder. In the process of loading a cannon, for example, a sufficient quantity had to be packed in from the muzzle with a long ram: if packed too tight, the fine powdery mixture would form into a solid mass, which was impermeable to the necessary propagation of the flame; if packed too loose, the charge would burn inefficiently or fizzle out; and if packed too carelessly, the gun could blow up. Then in the sixteenth century, the black powder makers evolved the process of "corning." This consisted of wetting and working the black powder mixture into a doughy mass which was then rolled, pressed, and ground into grains of preselected size. These grains would now retain their composition and geometry. Thus there was no longer danger of the sulfur settling out with the resulting unpleasant necessity for mixing gunpowder in the heat of battle. Gunners then began to learn that optimum performance was obtained by tailoring the grain size, and thus the speed of total combustion, to their particular gun (the reasons for this are explored in Chapter 5).

Subsequent modifications came about principally in standardization of manufacture. Inevitably in the course of time, this simple mixture developed to a point where it was consistent and safe. The proper grain size for each type of weapon was established empirically, and eventually the optimum charge for any given type of weapon was determined. Black powder, basically unaltered with the years, remained predominantly in use until the end of the last century and, in fact, was employed as a principal propellant for the weapons of the Spanish-American War. However, by that time, modern propellants had virtually made it obsolete. Today black powder is used mainly in the manufacture of pyrotechnics. And so, in a sense, the uses of black powder have reverted back to their original employment for flash and noise, for now a substantial portion of every year's production is happily blown up in celebration of the glorious Fourth.

## EVOLUTION OF THE GUN

Berthold the Black, according to the legend, dramatically stumbled across the idea for his invention of a gun while mixing the ingredients of black powder with a mortar and pestle. The mixture was accidentally ignited and the directed force of the explosion hurled the pestle against the ceiling. Unfortunately, there is no reliable documentary evidence to confirm the story; the time of the incident is indefinite, and even the legend itself has various versions. One variation of this account has it that Friar Berthold, called "the Black" by his colleagues because of his dabblings in the mysteries of alchemy, was blown to bits while demonstrating the powers of his mixture. There is also a story that he was imprisoned for his wicked proficiency in alchemy, allegedly obtained directly from Satan, that he conducted his black powder experiments in his prison cell, and that he was later executed. Since there is no proof that the unfortunate friar ever made a gun, and since there are no others with a better claim to the gun's invention, there is much uncertainty as to its origin. However, even though the very early history of guns is hazy, it does appear that a gun, used to fire a projectile, was employed as early as 1313, and there are many references to the use of guns prior to 1350. The beginning of the history of guns can thus be placed as probably sometime in the early fourteenth century. However, before proceeding with the ensuing development of guns, a distinction should be made between artillery and handguns. The subsequent evolution of the gun, moreover, can be more easily followed by considering each of these two types individually.

Artillery, defined roughly, includes all guns too heavy for a man to carry. In the very early days, artillery pieces were nothing more than large crude tubes made of wrought iron or of iron bars hooped together with iron rings. Originally these heavy pieces were mounted on heavy wooden frames, and wedges were employed to hold the tube at a desired angle of elevation. Their limited mobility depended on clumsy sledges, which were pulled by horses, oxen, or brute manpower. An early improvement was the casting of gun barrels in one piece with two protrusions (or trunnions), which facilitated mounting on a wheeled carriage; by locating these trunnions near the tube's center of gravity the gun's elevation could be easily changed. But once the technique for casting bronze cannon had been developed in the late fifteenth century, there was no really significant improvement in artillery pieces for some three hundred years. The casting of heavy gun tubes was a very costly enterprise requiring the establishment of big gun-foundries and the use of great quantities of metals which were not always easily available. Accordingly, there was little disposition to changing the basic design, which for centuries was simply a smooth bored tube loaded from the muzzle.

Whereas the costly and cumbersome nature of artillery inhibited innovation, handguns were much more easily adaptable to experimental modification. A handgun, as opposed to an artillery piece, is a gun that can be carried and fired by one man. Because of its much smaller size and its more modest demands on material and manufacturing costs, the handgun was correspondingly more susceptible to change and improvement. Even with the uncertainty of their trial-and-error methods, the efforts of countless inventors, innovators, and artisans caused the hand firearm to pass through a much more varied, colorful, and rapid development. Accordingly, the larger part of the history of guns is the story of the evolution of handguns, or small arms as they are known today.

In its early days, the original handgun, shown in Figure 1, was an awkward and dangerous object. It did not really evolve into a workable gun until certain improvements were made. By the fifteenth century, the gun had been made much less awkward to use and it had a much easier means for igniting the propellant. The barrel was now fastened onto a wooden stock with a curved butt to fit the shoulder, so that a shooter could hold the gun in a manner that permitted him to sight along the barrel at his target. Easier ignition was accomplished with the first "trigger," which was a curved piece of metal pivoted onto the stock. One end of this piece held a match, which was simply a length of cord, or wick, that had been impregnated with saltpeter and could therefore remain ignited and burn slowly. The other end was at first moved by hand and eventually held by a spring-loaded trigger. When actuated, the burning wick end would be brought into contact with the powder at the touchhole. In this first configuration with a mechanical moving part, the gun was known as a matchlock. It was still very cumbersome, and the act of getting the gun loaded and ready to fire was not quick and easy. A small idea of its awkwardness can be seen from Plate 1, taken from an old manual of arms, which shows a few of the many steps necessary for getting the gun ready to fire. The man was not only encumbered with his heavy gun, but needed to carry pouches for projectiles and for powder, as well as for other paraphernalia. On top of this, he faced the further disadvantage of not always having time for a second shot if the first one missed. Nevertheless, he did have a very lethal weapon. This type of gun, for example, played a heavy role in the conquest of the New World, for its flash, thunderous noise, and terrible effectiveness led the indigenous American inhabitants to believe they were facing supernatural beings.

The invention of mechanical clocks in the thirteenth century and their rapid development during the early Renaissance stimulated a great interest in complicated mechanisms. Inevitably the skill of the craftsman and the ingenuity of the clockmaker were directed to gun mechanisms. As a result, there developed, about 1515, a very much improved gun ignition system—the wheel lock. This ingenious and completely mechanical device was a great improvement over the crude matchlock with its glowing rope. The heart of this new mechanism was a coil spring, of the type developed for use in clocks, which was set into a box located in the wooden stock. The powder pan along the touchhole was fitted with a sliding cover, into which projected the periphery of a toothed wheel. The spring was wound by means of a special key and then a hinged lever, or cock, was tilted into the pan. The cock itself held a piece of iron pyrite against the toothed wheel, which was now loaded by the coiled spring. When the trigger was actuated, the toothed wheel spun against the iron pyrite very much like the action of a cigarette lighter today, and the sparks ignited the powder in the pan. This wheel lock had many advantages over the matchlock. Since the gun could be cocked, the shooter needed only to concern himself with his target and then only had to perform the simple act of aiming and squeezing the trigger. The mechanical geniuses of the time, who either made clocks, locks, or gun mechanisms, were even then concerned with methods of miniaturizing their devices. The wheel lock was made smaller and therefore adaptable for use not only in shoulder-fired guns, but in pistols as well. By virtue of its very portability and simple employment, the pistol could be used by a horseman. For the first time now, here was a gun that was easy to carry, easy to use, and very reliable. Nevertheless, it also had its disadvantages. For one, it was much more expensive than the matchlock. Also, since the mechanism was complicated, it could not stand much rough handling and had to be kept clean and free from rust. But perhaps its biggest disadvantage was the consequence of a common frailty: gunners were always losing their keys.

The wheel lock was a wonderful mechanism for its time, but its expense and delicate complexity led to a need for a more rugged, but nonetheless just as effective a mechanism. For a century or so there was a proliferation of designs, and gunsmiths all across Europe were striving—many with success—to develop improved mechanisms. However, it was not until the early seventeenth century that a real lasting improvement was made with the development of the flintlock. This at last was a first-rate development, for it combined the mechanical ingenuity of the best devices of the time with ruggedness, simplicity of design, and almost foolproof reliability. Its operation was very straightforward. In action, the cock, with a piece of flint in its jaws, would strike the L-shaped

33298

flashpan cover, and in so doing would cam open the cover and deliver the sparks to the flashpan all in one movement. This obviated a difficulty that had existed with all previous guns, which suffered from the fact that, once the pan cover was opened, rain could get in and soak the pan and touchhole powder before it could get ignited. For the next two hundred years, the flintlock, in shoulder gun and in pistol, remained the finest, most reliable of all small arms.

Still, there was a need for something less primitive than the collision of flint and steel to generate the igniting spark. Then, during the War of 1812, Joshua Shaw, an American inventor, developed the percussion cap. This was a small closed cup-shaped copper piece filled with the newly discovered fulminate of mercury, a substance that explodes and flashes into flame when struck sharply. By changing the flashpan and the touchhole to a nipple with an inner passage to the propellant charge, and by placing the inverted cup over the nipple, the gun could now be fired by simply striking the cap. The act of squeezing the trigger would then release the cock, which because of its "hammering" action was henceforth to be called a hammer. The spring-loaded hammer would then strike the cap with sufficient force to actuate the fulminate. Percussion cap ignition, which was a great improvement over flint and steel, very quickly became standardized, and by the time of the American Civil War had effectively replaced flintlock ignition.

The gun had gone through quite a radical evolution in its progression from the early crude tubes, ignited by a hot iron or a glowing rope, to the handsome, mechanically efficient, percussion-fired weapons of a century ago. Yet for all these improvements, one basic feature of all firearms remained essentially unaltered. This was the method of loading from the muzzle. To load his gun, a shooter first poured a desired quantity of propellant powder into the muzzle. Then he added his projectile, which in time was enclosed by a patch of thin cloth to ensure a tight fit. Finally, he employed a ramrod to push the bullet down and seat it firmly against the powder. With time, he learned to prepackage his propellant into individual containers, usually of paper, to guarantee a uniform amount of propellant and to make the loading operation a little more convenient. Although many gunsmiths had come up with very workable breech-loaded weapons, these weapons were unable to stand up under the repeated violence of the explosions and eventually began to come apart. Other than a very small diameter touchhole, openings or fissures in any form in the vicinity of the powder charge were simply not feasible. Accordingly, muzzle loading continued to be the predominant procedure for loading weapons until the end of the American Civil War.

The revolutionary improvement over muzzle loading finally came with the development of the cartridge—a complete, easily handled breech-loading package, containing the ignition system, the metal casing, the bullet, and the propellant. Ever since the discovery of fulminate of mercury as an igniting or "priming" material, many inventors had tried to design a cartridge. The first successful attempt was made in 1855 by Smith and Wesson, with their metallic cartridge, containing the fulminate of mercury inside a flared rim. When the rim was struck by a firing pin, the fulminate flashed and ignited the propellant. This cartridge, however, was not completely reliable but, in 1866, Colonel Hiram Berdan developed a working cartridge, which in its essential features is still used. A full metal case contains the propellant and the bullet. In the center of the base there is a receptacle for the primer, which is an assembly consisting of a soft metal cup containing a pellet of priming material and a small hard metallic "anvil." When the hammer strikes the primer, the pellet of priming mix is crushed and ignites the propellant charge.

Berdan's all-metal center-fire cartridge made possible, in 1873, the development of the first reliable repeating rifle, the lever-action Winchester 73. This gun, which came to be known as "the gun that won the West," was truly remarkable for its time. It was very accurate and could shoot just as fast as a man could actuate the lever. This combination of cartridge and repeating rifle was a truly revolutionary development because the shooter could load a dozen cartridges into the magazine and could then shoot at will with no effort, except for aiming the gun and actuating the lever. Performance, moreover, was reliable and ballistically reproducible from shot to shot. The over-all effectiveness of the weapon is underscored by an encounter between Buffalo Bill Cody and a bear. The wounded bear had managed to charge toward him from a distance of some thirty feet, but Mr. Cody managed to pump eleven shots into him during the few seconds of his charge and, of course, survived to tell the tale.

Buffalo Bill's performance is even more interesting when it is realized that the eleven cartridges he fired were all filled with a simple mixture of sulfur, saltpeter, and charcoal. The formula for this mixture was by no means new, for it had been written down by a studious monk more than six hundred years before.

## THE DEVELOPMENT OF MODERN PROPELLANTS

The history of modern propellants dates from 1846, when Christian Schönbein, a German chemistry professor at Basel, announced his discovery of nitrocellulose, or guncotton. He obtained nitrocellulose by impregnating cotton fibers, which are practically pure cellulose, in a mixture of nitric acid and sulfuric acid. The resulting nitrated cellulose was found to have very interesting properties. When burned, it decomposed completely into gaseous products with the release of an enormous amount of heat. Since guncotton contained three times as much energy as black powder, its potential as a new propellant was quickly appreciated. Schönbein immediately began experiments with his new substance and, in July of that same year, he actually fired a cannon loaded with guncotton and a projectile. However, the use of nitrocellulose as a propellant presented many difficulties: the thin fibers would burn so rapidly that enormous pressures would develop in a gun; it was also found, from many disastrous explosions, that residual acid in the nitrocellulose made it very unstable. For years there were frustratingly unsuccessful attempts to tame this potentially superior material. Finally, in 1884, the clue to making nitrocellulose a satisfactory propellant was found by Paul Vieille, a French physicist. He eliminated the fibrous structure of the nitrocellulose by treating it in a mixture of ether and alcohol, which gelatinized the substance into an easily workable pasty mass. This could be rolled into sheets of desired thickness, dried, and then cut up into strips or squares. The real value of this new propellant was immediately recognized by the French Army, which designated it Poudre B.

Another event that made the year 1846 historically important in the development of modern propellants was the discovery of nitroglycerin by the Italian chemist, Ascanio Sobrero. Nitroglycerin, by itself, is completely unsuitable as a propellant because its decomposition is instantaneous and would shatter a gun. However, it can be made an effective ingredient of a propellant. In 1888, Alfred Nobel, the Swedish chemist, famous for his invention of dynamite and his funding of the Nobel Prize, came up with a variation on the use of nitrocellulose. He used nitroglycerin as a material to effect gelatinization of the nitrocellulose. Again, the gelatinous mass was rolled and cut in the same way as Poudre B. This new propellant was named ballistite. On the heels of Poudre B and ballistite, activities everywhere became intensified. Not to be outdone, the English developed a method for mixing nitrocellulose with nitroglycerin and then bringing gelatinization about by means of acetone. In this case, however, the resulting mass was not rolled out in sheets, but was extruded through holes in a plate to form long cords, which were cut to desired lengths. This propellant thus came to be known as cordite. Although there were further modifications and improvements, the basic ingredients of modern gun propellants had been established. Many, like Poudre B, were primarily nitrocellulose and these have come to be known as single-base propellants. Others, like ballistite and cordite, have both nitrocellulose and nitroglycerin as primary constituents, and these have come to be known as double-base propellants. Granular gun propellants today are still classified as being either single- or double-base.

The essential chemical and physical properties of many of today's gun propellants are not greatly different than those of the three early modern propellants: Poudre B, ballistite, and cordite. However, a propellant with unique characteristics was developed in Illinois by Fred Olsen in 1933, with his invention of the process for making ball powder. As the name implies, the individual grains are not extruded or rectangular, but are small, closely sized spheres, which, depending on the application, are more or less flattened by mechanical rolling. The manufacturing processes for this propellant, interestingly enough, all take place under water. In manufacture, the nitrocellulose is dissolved in ethyl acetate, a solution of nitroglycerin is added, and the resulting lacquer-like material is broken up under water into a multiplicity of spheres, much like the spheres that result if one puts some oil into a bottle of water and shakes it vigorously. Although basically a double-base propellant, it has some unusual properties, which make it particularly suitable for many specific purposes. One of these, for example, is its use as the propellant in U. S. Infantry small arms ammunition.

Compared to black powder, modern gun propellants have some tremendous advantages: they are very safe to handle; they can be manufactured with precise, prechosen chemical and physical characteristics; they are completely converted into gaseous products (unlike black powder, which leaves bore residue and generates a lot of smoke); and they are much more powerful. Had Buffalo Bill faced that irate bear armed with a modern rifle and with smokeless powder cartridges, he could have delivered—with just two or three shots—the same total killing energy that took eleven cartridges filled with black powder.

## INTERIOR BALLISTICS FROM ART TO SCIENCE

The history of guns and propellants had its beginnings over six centuries ago. By virtue of much mechanical ingenuity and countless trial-and-error modifications, the gun, by the mid-nineteenth century, had been developed to a high degree of effectiveness and reliability. Yet this all took place in spite of the fact that, at best, there was a very limited and vague understanding of what actually took place inside a gun. The individuals who designed, built, and used guns knew little more of the appropriate scientific principles than those early monks who first wrote out formulas for black powder. Interior ballistics as a science simply did not exist. The amount of available knowledge was based completely on hard-won empirical relationships. Nevertheless, although these relationships were not very exact, they could be made to work. The more artful gunner, for example, would know about how much propellant he would need in order to make his projectile travel a given range. Although he had no knowledge of the velocity of the projectile, he did know that if more than a given quantity of propellant were used the results would be more disastrous to himself than to the enemy. He also had a working knowledge of the effects of powder granulation and the importance of proper bore clearance. Thus, although the gunner did not understand the process inside a gun, he was able to control it.

For the first four hundred years, there was no great concern over the general ignorance about interior ballistics. After black powder could be made to behave in a reasonably consistent manner, the chief preoccupation was in making guns more accurate and in improving their mechanism. Almost no attention was paid to the processes inside a gun. It made little difference anyway, because they could not be understood without first finding a means of obtaining some quantitative measurements. During this time, there existed no knowledge of the pressures in a gun or of the muzzle velocity of the projectile. The first big step in this direction occurred in England in 1742, when Benjamin Robins invented the ballistic pendulum and successfully used it to obtain accurate measurements of the velocities of musket balls. From physical principles, he then tried to estimate the peak pressure in the gun, basing his procedure on the average pressure that would have been necessary to give him this velocity. His *New Principles of Gunnery,* which he published in that same year, is perhaps the first book that treated the problem of ballistic performance and first stated the fundamental problem of interior ballistics, namely the achievement of a given muzzle velocity without exceeding a prohibitive pressure in the gun. Progress, however, remained terribly slow and it was over a hundred years before another British artillerist, Sir Andrew Noble, invented a workable pressure gauge in 1860. Now at last there were reliable methods to measure the peak pressure in a gun and the muzzle velocity of a projectile with a reasonable degree of precision.

With these capabilities for measuring muzzle velocity and peak pressure, the foundations for developing some basic knowledge about what takes place in a gun during firing were now firmly laid. The next important advance in measuring techniques was made by the same Vieille who first successfully made smokeless powder, when he invented a rotating recording crusher gauge with which pressure could be measured as it varies with time during the total interval the projectile travels in the gun. An understanding of phenomena in a gun was also helped by the fact that the new smokeless propellants were more easily controlled in manufacture and could be more accurately described by shape and size. The new propellants, however, by virtue of their greater power, had exaggerated the basic ballistic problem: i.e., to determine an optimum balance between maximum velocity and peak pressure level. With a well-made barrel, it was virtually impossible to blow up a gun with an overload of black powder. However, this was not the case with the new smokeless propellants which could develop much higher pressures. An excessive propellant charge, or the use of a propellant that burned too quickly, could easily mean a shattered barrel. It was found, moreover, that ballistic performance was greatly affected by the geometry and the chemical composition of the propellant grain. A fundamental knowledge of interior ballistics had, therefore, now become a necessity.

A need to understand the critical performance characteristics of these powerful new propellants prompted a great deal of research and experimental activity in interior ballistics. This was facilitated by the vastly improved measuring techniques now available, and by the greater knowledge of chemistry and thermodynamics. Finally, around the turn of the century, a French ballistician, Paul Charbonnier, put together a series of equations which described the interior ballistics process. This, in a true sense, marked the real beginnings of interior ballistics as a science. However, now that the problems had been posed and were found to be solvable mathematically, there was a further need not only to solve, but also to explain why propellants behaved as they did in a gun. In the last few decades the advances in this direction have been enormous. Today, with highly developed and sophisticated measuring techniques, with a very firm foundation in chemistry, thermodynamics, and physics, and with the assistance of high-speed digital computers, complex phenomena inside a gun are not only well understood, but accurately predictable.

## CHAPTER 2

# THE CHEMISTRY OF PROPELLANTS

Anyone who succumbs to a carnival's air of fun and excitement and joins the noisy throng shuffling down the midway to the music of the incessant steam calliope will eventually be drawn toward the sharp staccato rhythms coming from the shooting gallery. The heart of this popular amusement is a complete round of ammunition in its smallest and simplest form; less than an inch long, it contains a mere pinch of propellant for driving a one-gram projectile that safely disintegrates on target impact. Yet for all the deceptive simplicity of this small cartridge, the chemical, thermodynamic, and physical phenomena that take place inside the gallery gun are in no essential respects different from those that take place inside a huge sixty-foot-long naval sixteen-inch rifle, when it hurls a ton of steel and TNT against a target twenty-eight miles away. The processes and underlying principles are basically the same in all guns, regardless of size or type. However, since most of us have a little familiarity with hand-held weapons, it will be more easily convenient if we henceforth explore the interesting mysteries of interior ballistics with the help of that class of small-caliber systems we call sporting arms and ammunition.

The study of interior ballistics is concerned with that sequence of events which take place during the interval of time from the instant of propellant ignition to the bullet's exit from the muzzle. Our purpose is therefore to scrutinize and then seek an understanding of the phenomena that occur in this infinitesimal time interval. For an easy visualization of the action that takes place in a gun barrel, we can make free use of our imagination and think of the action as a sort of three-act drama. In the first act, the dormant granules of propellant, aroused to violent reaction by a shooting flame from the primer, begin their chemical transformation into various gaseous substances. In the second act, the rate at which the hot gases are generated is greatly increased and, confined as they are in a small volume, they begin to exert enormous pressures. To keep these pressures from exceeding the strength limits of the gun, the projectile must now begin to move and provide a larger volume. In the final act, these pressures accelerate the projectile down the bore, and in the process the energy stored in the hot gases is finally converted to the kinetic energy of the projectile and the recoil energy of the gun. The drama concludes as the projectile hurtles into the atmosphere and the gun is forcibly shoved into the shooter's resilient shoulder.

The purpose of this chapter is to develop some understanding of the basic character of the principal performer, in this case the propellant, and then to describe those events that take place in the first act. As our story begins we will observe the process that converts a stable substance, like cotton, into one with tremendous explosive power. However, as the mild substance is transformed into a powerful one, it also develops an unpredictable inner urge to unleash its energies without provocation. Accordingly, a secondary treatment will be necessary to inhibit this dangerous instability—a treatment which consists basically of incorporating a sort of "tranquilizer" into the material. The end product will then be completely safe and reliable; it will release its power only on command and it will do so in a predictable and controlled manner. After the material has taken on all its desired characteristics, it is finally ready to perform as a propellant. The first act will come to an explosive conclusion as we watch the solid granules of propellant decompose completely into various gases while they simultaneously release an enormous amount of heat. However, before the curtain goes up, a brief prologue is necessary to give an appropriate background in the form of a few simple but fundamental chemical principles.

## ATOMS, MOLECULES, AND RADICALS

All matter in the universe is composed of basic substances, or elements, of which over a hundred have so far been identified. *Atoms,* as understood in modern explanations of the structure of matter, are the smallest divisions into which any one of these elements can be broken down without changing its properties. Thus every known substance is constructed from one or more of these hundred or so different kinds of basic building blocks. For the structure of gun propellants only four different ones are necessary. These are the atoms of carbon, oxygen, hydrogen, and nitrogen. The two simple things to remember about them are their designation, or symbol, and their atomic weight.

TABLE 1

| Element | Symbol | Actual Atomic Weight | We Will Henceforth Call It |
|---|---|---|---|
| Carbon | C | 12.011 | 12 |
| Oxygen | O | 16.000 | 16 |
| Hydrogen | H | 1.008 | 1 |
| Nitrogen | N | 14.008 | 14 |

Although the third column gives the accurate values of atomic weight, the values in the last column are much more convenient and their use causes but a trivial loss in accuracy.

About thirty of the elements, notably the metals, can

occur in nature in a free, or uncombined, state. These same elements can also combine with the atoms of other elements to form substances with entirely different properties. Carbon, for example, can exist either in its uncombined elemental form or it can be a constituent element in an almost infinite number of combinations with other elements. On the other hand, there are some elements, like hydrogen, oxygen, and nitrogen, that occur naturally only in combinations with one or more atoms of their own or of a different element. Those stable combinations that are formed by one or more atoms are called *molecules*. The following seven simple molecules will play a prominent part in the ensuing story.

| Molecule | | Molecular Weight |
|---|---|---|
| $H_2$ | Hydrogen | 2 |
| $N_2$ | Nitrogen | 28 |
| $O_2$ | Oxygen | 32 |
| $CO$ | Carbon monoxide | 28 |
| $CO_2$ | Carbon dioxide | 44 |
| $H_2O$ | Water | 18 |
| $HNO_3$ | Nitric acid | 63 |

The first six of these are important because they constitute the gaseous products of propellant decomposition (water is normally a liquid but at explosion temperatures it exists only in gaseous form). Although a simple-looking molecule, the seventh one, nitric acid, deserves special mention. It plays quite a different role, for it is the unique action of nitric acid on certain relatively innocuous substances that converts them to explosives.

Atoms from two or more elements can also combine to form a different kind of atomic structure—the *radical*. A radical differs from a molecule in that it does not exist freely by itself but is always a constituent part or substructure of a more complex molecule. A radical can therefore be considered as a sort of prefabricated unit used for building larger molecules. Two radicals are of particular interest in the formation of explosives: the simple hydroxyl radical, OH, which is merely one atom each of oxygen and hydrogen; and the nitrate radical, which is one atom of nitrogen attached to three atoms of oxygen. The nitrate radical has a structure which the chemist can represent in a variety of ways, such as:

$$O\text{---}N \begin{matrix} O \\ \\ O \end{matrix} \text{, or } O\text{-}NO_2 \text{, or } ONO_2 \text{, or just } NO_3$$

If a hydrogen atom attaches to the hydroxyl radical, the result is HOH, or $H_2O$, a water molecule. Or if a hydrogen atom attaches to the nitrate radical, the result is $HNO_3$, a nitric acid molecule.

The action of a nitric acid molecule on a hydroxyl radical gives a nitrate radical and a molecule of water. This reaction can be written as:

$$HNO_3 + OH \longrightarrow ONO_2 + H_2O$$

At this point it should be noted that it is this one simple reaction that is the vital key to the formation of all explosives.

## BUILDING THE UNSTABLE STRUCTURE

The principal character in our drama begins as cellulose, a chemically stable substance occurring abundantly in all parts of the vegetable kingdom. It is the principal structural material of cell wall, wood fiber, and the tissues of all plant life. Cotton fibers, in particular, are an almost pure form of cellulose. Cellulose is also a member of several broad chemical categories: it is an organic compound, a carbohydrate, and a polymer. It is an organic compound because it belongs to that class of substances whose molecules contain carbon and hydrogen, but which may also contain additional elements such as oxygen, nitrogen, and some others. The molecules of organic compounds also possess unique structural characteristics. In all organic compounds, the atoms of carbon act as principal corner stones and they are mortared to each other, and to the other atoms in the structure, by chemical bonds. Cellulose is a carbohydrate, because its molecules are made up of the three elements, carbon, hydrogen, and oxygen, and because, just as in the water molecule, there are twice as many hydrogen as oxygen atoms. Cellulose is a polymer because each of its molecules consists of thousands of identical structures, such as the one shown at the top of Figure 2, all linked together like paper clips.

The conversion of this stable substance into an explosive occurs when the cellulose comes into contact with nitric acid. When this happens, each nitric acid molecule promptly reacts with one of the hydroxyl groups. The resulting reaction generates one molecule of water and causes a nitrate radical to replace the hydroxyl group. The bottom of Figure 2 shows how this reaction modifies the cellulose molecule. However, since the creation of each hydroxyl group is accompanied by the creation of one molecule of water, a large quantity of water will eventually be produced. As these reactions continue, enough water is released to dilute the nitric acid, and this can slow down the chemical process. To prevent this undesirable dilution of the acid, some mechanism is necessary for mopping up the water as fast as it is generated. It so happens this is an activity for which sulfuric acid is uniquely well suited. Sulfuric acid and water molecules have an affinity for each other that causes the sulfuric acid molecules to become attached to the water molecules. In a way, the sulfuric acid acts as if it were a

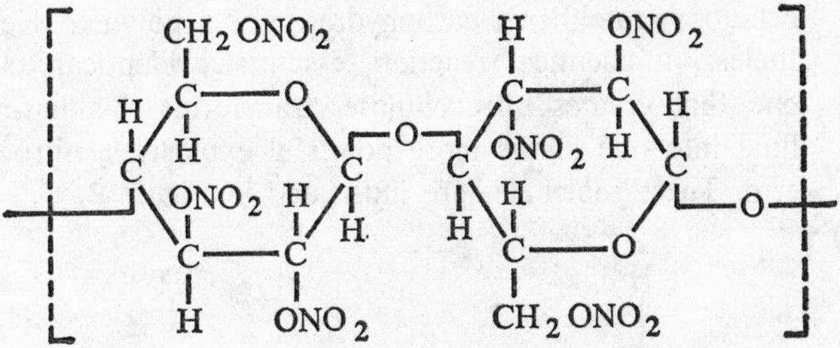

Fig. 2. Conversion of cellulose to nitrocellulose: (a) A cellulose molecule is a long chain with thousands of identical links. Each link is a complex arrangement of carbon, hydrogen, and oxygen atoms with a structure represented by diagram A. (b) When cellulose is acted upon by nitric acid, each of the OH groups is converted to an $ONO_2$ group. Thus after the nitration, which converts cellulose to cellulose nitrate (nitrocellulose), each link in the molecule has the new structure shown in diagram B.

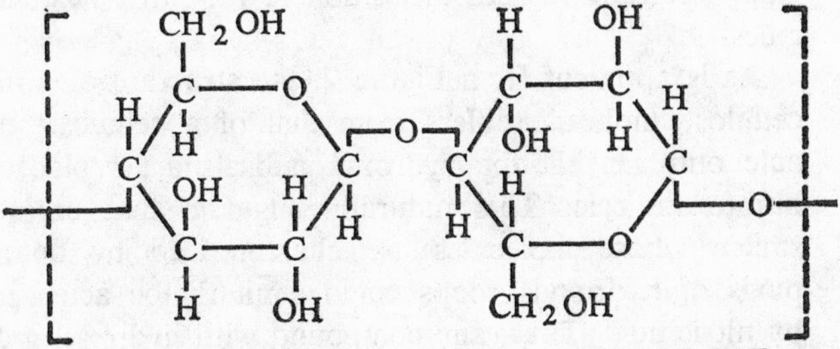

liquid sponge, for it absorbs the water and prevents it from interference with the action of the nitric acid molecules.

As is apparent from Figure 2, the structure of a nitrocellulose molecule differs from that of a cellulose molecule only in that the hydroxyl radicals are replaced by nitrate radicals. This naturally suggests that any substance whose molecules are characterized by outcroppings of hydroxyl groups could similarly be acted upon by nitric acid. Thus, any compound with hydroxyl groups might be considered a candidate for conversion into an explosive. This happens to be perfectly true. We can now introduce into this drama a second performer that also starts off as a chemically stable and relatively innocuous substance. It is also an organic compound, but unlike cellulose is neither a carbohydrate nor a polymer. Nevertheless, a chemical reaction, essentially identical to the one that creates nitrocellulose, transforms this harmless fluid into one of the more powerful explosives, nitroglycerin. These molecules are illustrated in Figure 3.

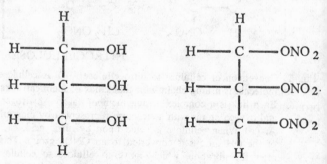

Fig. 3. Conversion of glycerin to nitroglycerin.

Again, it is the action of nitric acid molecules on the three hydroxyl radicals in the glycerin molecule that changes them to nitrate radicals and thus converts glycerin to glycerin trinitrate, as nitroglycerin is more properly known.

## MAKING THE STRUCTURE STABLE

The early history of the uses of nitrocellulose as a propellant was plagued by its unpredictable and dangerous instability. After Schönbein announced his discovery of guncotton in Basel in May 1846, he promptly set about with experiments to explore its explosive capabilities. Two short months later he actually fired a cannon that used guncotton to propel a projectile. The military implications of his discovery were immediately recognized and enthusiastically pursued. In that very same year, he conducted experiments at government arsenals both in Germany and in England. Yet, in the midst of the general preoccupation with military applications, he did not overlook the peaceful uses of guncotton, for he also employed it to blow up some old walls at Basel, to blast rocks in southern Germany, and even to perform experiments in the mines of Cornwall. The universal enthusiasm for this powerful new substance, however, was soon shattered by a large number of terrible explosions. Very soon after the manufacture of guncotton was begun, a plant in England unexplainably blew up with the loss of twenty-one lives, and in France two more plants exploded with disastrous consequences. Although this brought the manufacture of guncotton in France and England to a sudden halt, the Austrians were not yet discouraged, and they started up a plant in 1853. All seemed well for a while, but ten years later a guncotton magazine blew up with no assignable cause. After a subsequent magazine explosion in 1865, the Austrians also threw up their hands and prohibited its further manufacture. These disasters almost stopped any further work on guncotton. A substance that could suddenly explode

without warning or evident cause was simply too dangerous for use. Nevertheless, its great potential utility, coupled with the unshakable preoccupation of the scientist
with a difficult problem, resulted in a vigorous determination to find the cause, and the cure, for this instability.

The first thing the chemists uncovered was that instability could result from minute quantities of residual
acid left in the guncotton during manufacture. The $ONO_2$
radicals that characterize nitrocellulose are formed from
nitric acid molecules. Yet, paradoxically, other nitric
acid molecules, when they come in contact with these
$ONO_2$ radicals, act to break them down. When one is
broken down, a nitrogen dioxide molecule, $NO_2$, is
formed and, at the same time, a small quantity of heat
is liberated. Furthermore, in the presence of moisture,
$H_2O$, in the air, the $NO_2$ combines with this $H_2O$ to give
$HNO_3$, and so more nitric acid is formed. Thus, as one
nitrate radical is broken down, it ends up as part of a
new nitric acid molecule that promptly goes to work to
break down another nitrate radical; this in turn results
in more nitric acid molecules to break down more nitrate
radicals and so a slow chain reaction is begun. When
the total heat released from all these individual reactions
finally builds up to a certain level, it can explode the
whole quantity of nitrocellulose. Accordingly, attempts
were soon devoted to more effective means of removing
the residual acid. The first step in this direction was made
by Sir Frederick Abel in England, when he introduced
the process of pulping. In this process, the wet nitrocellulose is converted into pulp with apparatus very much
like that used for the manufacture of paper. The pulping
actually cuts the cotton fibers down into much shorter
lengths and also helps break open the tubular recesses
in the fibers from which the acid is so difficult to remove.

The more efficient methods for acid removal were a
great first step, but they were not quite enough. A nitro-

cellulose molecule is basically unstable and has a built-in inclination to decompose, i.e., to have its $ONO_2$ radicals break down. In actuality, the rate at which $NO_2$ is formed in well-purified nitrocellulose is so very slow that it would have no important effect were it not for the chain reaction it sets up in the presence of normal air moisture. Accordingly, the real secret to making it stable is to add a material that can absorb the $NO_2$ molecules as fast as they are produced. In this manner, the nitrocellulose may lose a trivially small part of its nitrogen content, but at least the chain reaction and the buildup of heat are eliminated. The chemists therefore set about to find a suitable material. They were not too quickly successful for, even with the improved processes for acid removal, the early stabilizers were not satisfactory. As late as 1907 the powder magazine on the French battleship *Jena* blew up, and again in 1911 the same thing happened on the battleship *Liberté*. Both explosions were imputed to spontaneous flammations of insufficiently stabilized nitrocellulose. Intensive research, principally in France, finally resulted in the discovery of an excellent stabilizer—diphenylamine. By incorporating no more than 1 or 2 per cent of this material into the propellant, it becomes completely "tranquilized." The way diphenylamine acts to absorb the $NO_2$ molecules as fast as they are formed can be easily seen by a representation of the reaction between one molecule of diphenylamine and two $NO_2$ molecules. This is shown in Figure 4.

What makes diphenylamine so admirable a stabilizer is that it will very promptly give up an H atom in exchange for an $NO_2$ molecule. Diphenylamine is thus the effective tranquilizer for giving the necessary stability to a nitrocellulose propellant without in any way reducing the propellant's tremendous energy. A further safeguard lies in the current practice of propellant surveillance. When a

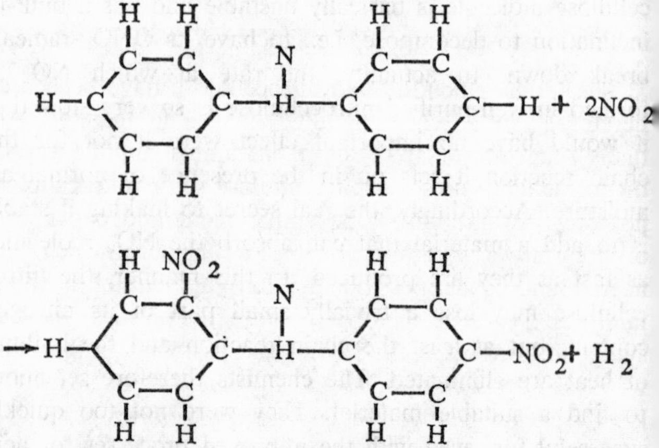

Fig. 4. Reaction of diphenylamine with $NO_2$.

lot of propellant is manufactured, a sample is stored under conditions that greatly accelerate the decomposition process. Continuous surveillance of this sample then determines the rate at which $NO_2$ is formed. Thus, if there is any incipient instability in a manufactured lot of propellant, it can be detected long before it will take place under normal conditions of usage.

Today there is no longer a real problem with the instability of propellants. Stabilizers and the practice of propellant surveillance have virtually removed all hazards in the storage of propellants. At worst, the propellant itself may lose a very small fraction of its chemical energy if the propellant is stored for long periods at elevated temperatures. Therefore, for all practical purposes, loaded ammunition can stand long storage periods without changes in its characteristics. Thus, the sportsman knows that he can purchase a box of ammunition and let it sit on a shelf for years with the comfortable assurance that it will remain absolutely safe and completely reliable.

## THE MANY FORMS OF THE STRUCTURE

The terms guncotton and nitrocellulose have been used heretofore in a seemingly interchangeable manner. Actually, guncotton is but one of an almost infinite variety of forms and uses of nitrocellulose. For nitrocellulose not only revolutionized the employment and capabilities of firearms, it was also the basic substance which pioneered and made possible the development of a whole family of synthetic materials. The early plastics, the first synthetic fibers, and the first successful photographic film were all nitrocellulose. The great versatility of nitrocellulose is due in part to certain characteristic properties resulting from the fact that it is a polymer. However, it is the variation in two attributes that provides nitrocellulose with its wide spectrum of physical properties: its percentage nitration, and the manner of its incorporation into a solvent. These two attributes are also of critical importance in the employment of nitrocellulose as a propellant.

Percentage nitration is simply a measure of the degree to which the cellulose is nitrated. The link of a nitrocellulose molecule, represented at the bottom of Figure 2, shows that every one of the six OH groups was replaced by an $ONO_2$ group. This link was therefore completely nitrated. For this case, the percentage nitration is obtained with simple arithmetic from the following tabulation, which sums up the number of atoms, by element, and their total atomic weight.

|  | No. of Atoms | Atomic Weight | Total Atomic Weight |
|---|---|---|---|
| Carbon | 12 | 12 | 144 |
| Hydrogen | 14 | 1 | 14 |
| Oxygen | 22 | 16 | 352 |
| Nitrogen | 6 | 14 | 84 |
|  |  |  | 594 |

The completely nitrated nitrocellulose molecule has 8 parts of nitrogen out of a total of 594 parts. This is 14.1 per cent. If, for example, only five of the six OH groups are replaced during nitration, then the link would show one OH and five $ONO_2$ groups. In this case, the following distribution would be obtained:

| | No. of Atoms | Atomic Weight | Total Atomic Weight |
|---|---|---|---|
| Carbon | 12 | 12 | 144 |
| Hydrogen | 15 | 1 | 15 |
| Oxygen | 20 | 16 | 320 |
| Nitrogen | 5 | 14 | 70 |
| | | | 549 |

Now with only 70 parts nitrogen out of a total of 549 the percentage nitration is found to be 12.75. Again, only four of the six OH groups are replaced by $ONO_2$ groups, a similar computation shows that the percentage nitration would then be 11.11. In practice, the nitration of cellulose is never complete. Although some links in each chain will be completely nitrated, some will have only five, some only four, or fewer, of the hydroxyl groups replaced by the nitrate radical. Thus the "percentage nitration" is a measure of the average degree to which the cellulose is nitrated. In commercial practice the highest obtainable percentage nitration is about 13.8. The lower useful limit is about 10.5 per cent, since nitrocellulose at any lower percentage nitration is not soluble in commercially available solvents in a manner giving useful physical properties.

Nitrocellulose in its raw fibrous form is a powerful, dangerous, and virtually useless substance. Guncotton, for example, is completely unsuitable as a propellant, for reasons given in the next chapter. It was not possible to exploit its potential as a propellant until Vieille altered its physical form by incorporating it into an ether-alcohol solution. As the nitrated cotton dissolved in the solution, it was converted into a gelatinous mass that had completely lost its fibrous texture. After Vieille rolled it out, the solvent evaporated and he was left with hardened, translucent sheets. He then cut these up and produced his celebrated Poudre B, the first successful smokeless propellant. Nitrocellulose, thus modified by a suitable solvent, could be given a wide spectrum of physical properties. The secret of its versatile utility derives from the metamorphosis that takes place when it is incorporated into a solvent. Transformed in this manner, nitrocellulose became the basic substance that led to two other major developments of modern times: plastics and synthetic fibers.

The birth of the plastics industry was precipitated by a curious need. About a hundred years ago the game of billiards was faced with a minor disaster. The only suitable substance with appropriate qualities for billiard balls was ivory. The demand for ivory, however, was so great that elephants couldn't be slaughtered fast enough to meet it. This disquieting situation prompted a billiard ball manufacturing concern to post a ten-thousand-dollar prize for the development of a satisfactory substitute substance. The prize was collected by John Hyatt, a young American printer, who together with his brother Isaiah first produced successful billiard balls in 1868 by dissolving nitrocellulose in a highly volatile solvent and incorporating it into camphor. The brothers quickly organized a company for the manufacture of this new material, which they called celluloid. This first commercially usable plastic found a great variety of uses—in combs, collars, piano keys, dolls, and many other articles. All the early motion picture films were made "on celluloid." Yet, since it was basically nitrocellulose, celluloid had an annoying and sometimes dangerous flammability. This led to the search for suitable plastic materials with the same admirable physical properties, but with a less flammable nature. Nevertheless, for half a century, plastics were predominantly celluloid.

At about the same time that Vieille developed his celebrated Poudre B, another French chemist, Count Hilaire de Chardonnet, first produced a practical synthetic fiber. He dissolved a nitrocellulose of about 11.8 per cent nitration in an ether-alcohol solution. By forcing this material through individual glass capillary tubes he produced filaments that were then drawn and collected on a spool. As the filaments were forced through the capillary orifices, the ether-alcohol evaporated and left nitrocellulose fibers. However, since they were nitrocellulose, the filaments were intensely flammable and so they were chemically denitrated in a way that would not alter their physical properties. When finally washed, bleached, and dried, these fibers were found to have a toughness and a luster that greatly simulated silk. This new artificial silk was called rayon.

In general, the many uses of nitrocellulose can be broken down into two broad categories: explosives, which today employ percentage nitrations between 12.6 and about 13.6; and all other uses, which use percentage nitrations between 10.5 and 12.3. The higher percentage nitrations are more naturally suitable for propellant explosives since these contain more chemical energy. For the nonexplosive application, the moderately low nitrations have the advantage of a larger number of usable solvents, while the lowest-nitrated celluloses have a much greater degree of thermoplasticity. A generalized relationship between percentage nitration, the appropriate solvents, and uses of nitrocellulose is summarized in the following table.

TABLE 2

| % Nitration | Solvent | Uses |
| --- | --- | --- |
| 10.5–11.2 | Alcohol | Celluloid plastics; lacquers |
| 11.2–12.3 | Ether alcohol; acetone, ethyl acetate; banana oil | Photographic films; lacquers; rayon; fingernail polish; artificial leather |
| 12.6–13.8 | Acetone | Explosives |

In spite of the varied nature of the many nitrocellulose end products, they still have fundamental similarities: propellant grains have mechanical properties and a physical appearance not too different from pieces of celluloid; a spherical granule of ball powder, for example, has an elasticity that would make it admirably suited for a billiard ball, if it were large enough; and even in manufacture, there are similarities between extruded propellants and rayon, since both are produced by forcing a fluid nitrocellulose through orifices. In fact, the process that Vieille used to fabricate his Poudre B can be simply visualized with the help of a common product found on every lady's dressing table—fingernail polish. This is generally nitrocellulose of low nitration in a fluid solution of one of the more pleasant-smelling volatile solvents, such as banana oil. As it is spread out over a surface, the solvent evaporates and leaves a thin sheet, or film. Although the hardened film will have too little nitration and too much pigment to qualify as a good propellant, nevertheless, if peeled off the surface, it can demonstrate that it is a close relative to a propellant by an easy ignitability and by the bright, instantaneous flash it can produce.

## COLLAPSE OF THE STRUCTURE

The whole purpose in following the steps that can transform cotton, or glycerin, into an explosive was to obtain a little insight into the basic nature of a gun propellant. In summary, the conversion of cellulose to a usable propellant has taken place in four stages. First, a chemical transformation converted the cellulose to nitrocellulose. Second, incorporation of the nitrocellulose into a suitable solvent eliminated its fibrous texture and changed it into a homogeneous, gelatinous mass. In the third stage, it was modified by the addition of a stabilizer, and perhaps also by a material to inhibit an undesirable tendency of propellants to absorb moisture. Finally, in the last stage, the propellant was physically formed into individual grains of a specified geometry, each of which contains chemical energy that is ready for instantaneous delivery on command. It is now time to observe the performance of a propellant as it unleashes its energy.

For purposes of showing the behavior of a propellant during decomposition, a nitrocellulose of 12.75 per cent nitration is selected, i.e., one which has an average of five nitrate groups per link. This structure can be represented as $C_{12}H_{15}O_{20}N_{10}$. However, to avoid the use of fractions, we will assume a structure composed of two links, i.e., $2C_{12}H_{15}O_{20}N_{10}$. The collapse of this structure will be triggered when enough heat is applied to bring any part of its surface temperature up to 340°F. The resulting process can be easily visualized if we think of it as taking place in five virtually instantaneous steps:

(1) as the reaction is triggered, the bonds that hold the structure together are broken and all the atoms are suddenly free;

(2) the thirty hydrogen atoms pair up to form fifteen $H_2$ molecules;

(3) each of the twenty-four carbon atoms takes an oxygen atom to form twenty-four CO molecules;

(4) the ten nitrogen atoms pair up to form five $N_2$ molecules;

(5) the remaining sixteen oxygen atoms combine with some of the $H_2$ and some of the CO molecules to produce $H_2O$ and $CO_2$ molecules.

At first, it might seem that the oxygen atoms, like the hydrogen and nitrogen, would pair up to give eight $O_2$ molecules. This does not happen because the oxygen is very much in demand by the fifteen $H_2$ molecules, each of which wants an additional oxygen atom to produce $H_2O$, and by the twenty-four CO molecules, each of which wants an additional oxygen atom to produce $CO_2$ molecules. However, with only sixteen oxygen atoms, but with a demand for thirty-nine, the $H_2$ and CO molecules must compete for the oxygen.

In actuality, the apportionment of the remaining oxygen atoms depends upon the temperature of the reaction. Thus, as the temperature changes, the oxygen atoms can flit back and forth from the $H_2$ to the CO molecules, a situation which is generally expressed by the so-called water-gas reaction.

$$H_2O + CO \longleftrightarrow H_2 + CO_2$$

In order to obtain an accurate quantitative distribution of the products of decomposition, the physical chemist will first determine the temperature of the reaction, and from this he will then establish the proper balance in the water-gas reaction. With cellulose of 12.75 per cent nitration, the actual reaction takes place at a temperature of 5200°F and, at this temperature, the equilibrium is such that roughly 63 per cent of the oxygen goes to the

$H_2$ (i.e., ten of the sixteen atoms), and so the reaction can be given as approximately:

$$2C_{12}H_{15}O_{20}N_{10} \longrightarrow 6CO_2 + 18CO + 10H_2O + 5H_2 + 5N_2 + \text{heat}$$

A quick look at the chemical reaction reveals an important point. All of the products of decomposition are gases ($H_2O$ is a gas at the resulting temperatures). Therefore there is no smoke or solid residue. For this reason, unlike the combustion of black powder, which produces a great deal of sooty residue and an enormous quantity of smoke, the nitrocellulose propellants came to be known as smokeless propellants. A second thing to note about the products of the reaction is the relatively high quantity of the still oxygen-hungry $H_2$ and CO. Since these gases leave the gun barrel at extremely high temperatures and since there is plenty of oxygen in the atmosphere, the gases will ignite as soon as they emerge. This ignition will then manifest itself as a bright muzzle flash. With a typical small arms rifle, this can be observed a few inches in front of the muzzle as a luminous flash about the size of a baseball. With an artillery piece, however, the flash can light up the countryside for miles. This is most objectionable, since it can give away the gun's position. For this reason some propellants, depending upon usage, may require an additional ingredient to help inhibit muzzle flash.

So far the discussion has centered on nitrocellulose. Although all gun propellants are based on nitrocellulose, a great many also contain nitroglycerin—thus the distinction between single-base propellants, which are based on nitrocellulose only, and double-base propellants, which are based on both nitrocellulose and nitroglycerin. Nitroglycerin is added mainly because it can increase the energy of the propellant. It also has the useful property of being a solvent for nitrocellulose. Its decomposition is quite similar to that of nitrocellulose:

$$2C_3H_5O_9N_3 \longrightarrow 6CO_2 + 5H_2O + 3N_2 + O_2 + heat$$

One apparent difference is that, in nitroglycerin, there is sufficient oxygen for the complete combustion of the carbon to carbon dioxide and the hydrogen to water.

The secret of a smokeless propellant's power derives from two characteristics of the decomposition process: the sudden and complete conversion of the solid granules into gases; and the heat generated by the chemical reaction, which raises the temperature of the confined gases and thus causes them to exert enormous pressures. The heat is generated during the individual reactions in which oxygen combines either with hydrogen to form water, or with carbon to form carbon monoxide or carbon dioxide. The clean-burning power of these propellants can be better appreciated by a comparison with the inefficient smoky combustion of black powders. The comparative performance between nitrocellulose of 12.75 per cent nitration and black powder is made easily apparent by comparing the results of the decomposition of one gram of each propellant.

| | Volume of Gas in Cubic Centimeters | Temperature of Reaction | % of Propellant Converted to Gases |
|---|---|---|---|
| Black powder | 270 | 3500°F | 44% |
| Nitrocellulose (12.75% N) | 900 | 5200°F | 100% |

In spite of the sharp contrast between these two propellants, their chemical reactions have interesting similarities. Black powder is a simple mechanical mixture of about 15 per cent charcoal, 75 per cent potassium nitrate, and 10 per cent sulfur. The charcoal, which is predominantly carbon, is the fuel while the potassium nitrate is the oxidizer. A potassium nitrate molecule, $KNO_3$, is actually an atom of potassium, K, attached to a nitrate radical. Thus part of the reaction that takes place in the smokeless propellant—namely the combining of carbon with oxygen, supplied by a nitrate group—is also the source for the heat generated during the combustion of black powder. A comparison of the propellants also points up a major distinction between propellant types. Black powder, since it is principally a mechanical mixture of fuel and oxidizer, is a primitive form of that class known as composite propellants. Smokeless propellants, on the other hand, are basically unstable compounds, and their fuel and oxidizer are in a sense built right into the molecule. Composite propellants have come into use in recent times because they have some characteristics which make them admirably suited as rocket propellants. With suitable plasticizers and other additives, they can be cast into large shapes of prechosen geometry, and they can maintain ignition at the low pressures characteristic of rocket motors. The inevitable solid residue of composite propellants, moreover, is not objectionable in a rocket since it is continuously discharged at the nozzle. Furthermore, by the use of the fuels which are much more efficient than the charcoal used in black powder, composite propellants today can compete with smokeless propellants in total energy content. However, when it comes to guns, where the propellant must burn controllably at very high pressures, where the propellant must also be rugged and easily storable, and where no solid residue is tolerable, the smokeless propellants are perfectly suited, whether it be in sixty-foot-long naval rifles, or in the gallery guns that add to the fun of every carnival.

# CHAPTER 3

# THERMODYNAMICS OF A GUN SYSTEM

One of the many miraculous deeds described in the ancient tales of the Arabian Nights occurred in the story of Aladdin and his wonderful lamp. This lamp had magical powers, for whenever it was stroked a great gust of smoke would roar out of the spout and transform itself into an enormous and powerful genie. There is a real counterpart to this fanciful story, for whenever a modern Aladdin squeezes a trigger he causes a firing pin to strike an initiating primer whose fingers of flame reach out to rouse another kind of genie that lies dormant in granules of propellant. It is this modern genie that plays the principal role in the second act of our drama. The first act showed the process of creation of a propellant and gave some insight into its basic nature. This second act will now show how this propellant is converted into a hot, gaseous form, how it then behaves, and how, like the faithful slave of the lamp, it unleashes its great energies and transforms them into useful work. Thus the purpose of this chapter is to examine the way a propellant's chemical energy is converted into heat, and then to observe the process by which this heat is in turn converted into the kinetic energy of a projectile's motion.

In order to describe these processes, it will be necessary to use the language and the concepts of *thermodynamics*. By definition, thermodynamics is the science that deals with the relationships between heat and energy and with the mechanism by means of which one is converted into the other. Accordingly, the principal objective of this chapter will be to describe the process that converts heat to mechanical energy and, specifically, how this all takes place inside a gun. However, in order to make this description intelligible, it needs the foundation of a few fundamental principles and definitions. These are provided in the early portion of this chapter, which begins with a discussion of the two simply expressed, but very fundamental laws which underlie all thermodynamic processes. This is followed by a definition of the basic quantities needed to describe a thermodynamic system. The way in which these quantities are interrelated, for any given state of the system, is next discussed, and finally some insight is given into the manner by which a system undergoes a change from one state to another. This background will provide a basis for understanding and appreciating the performance of our genie who, after his infinitesimally brief existence, partially transforms himself again into the energy of a high-velocity projectile.

## THE LAWS OF THERMODYNAMICS

Man's earliest formalized notions about the nature of the physical world were those expressed by the early Greek philosophers who conceived all matter as a combination of four basic constituent substances: earth, air, water, and fire.* In spite of the primitive simplicity of this speculation, more sophisticated ideas of fire and heat were not to appear for another two thousand years. Although it was known that fire made heat and heat caused a body to become warm, a reasonable concept of temperature did not exist, principally because there was no means for its measurement. The first meaningful step toward an understanding of heat was taken when Galileo

* Some philosophers speculated that the stars and planets were composed of a special fifth substance. This celestial fifth element, or essence, was therefore known as the "quintessence."

constructed his air thermoscope, which could measure changes in temperature. This device consisted of an air-filled glass bulb with a tube that dipped into a colored fluid. An increase in temperature caused expansion of the air, which in turn forced the fluid to rise a measurable amount. Although it was crude and suffered from the fact that it was just as sensitive to barometric pressure as it was to temperature, it nevertheless prompted the subsequent development of more accurate thermometers which indicated temperature by the relative expansion of a fluid, such as alcohol or mercury. The availability of consistent and accurate thermometers coupled with the quickened scientific curiosity of the eighteenth century led inevitably to intensive speculations about the nature of heat. This activity finally culminated with the workable (but erroneous) Caloric Theory of Heat, which hypothesized heat as a weightless, elusive, and invisible fluid that could flow in or out of a body and thereby make its temperature rise or fall. It was a theory that quickly divided the scientific world into zealous adherents and bitter foes. Fortunately, their disputations led to a great deal of argument and experiment, and thus to positive factual knowledge. By the middle of the nineteenth century, scientists had disproven the Caloric Theory and, in so doing, had learned two very fundamental things about the nature of heat.

First, it was learned that heat is simply a form of energy. An early clue to this was discovered by the self-taught Benjamin Thompson.† In 1798, while supervising the boring of brass cannon in Munich, he observed that

† A native of Massachusetts, Thompson's royalist sympathies prompted a prudent departure to England during the American Revolution. His adventurous career subsequently took him to Germany, where he became Minister of War in the service of Prince Maximilian of Bavaria, who also gave him a title, Count Rumford, and the opportunity to apply his considerable scientific abilities.

a great quantity of heat was released in the process. He also observed that he could create heat this way almost without limit by continued boring. From this he correctly deduced that much of the mechanical work was being converted directly into heat. The creation of heat by mechanical friction was not a new phenomenon. For an indeterminable number of centuries, primitive peoples had used the friction of wood on wood to start their fires. Thompson, moreover, was not the first man to realize that boring a cannon barrel caused it to become hot. However, he was a scientist who was preoccupied with the then current controversy over the Caloric Theory. Accordingly, he was quick to recognize a meaningful clue and was able to fathom the real meaning behind his simple observation. Thompson's conclusions were further corroborated in a quantitative manner by James Joule, an English physicist with a passion for accurate measurement. Joule showed by direct experiment that in all cases where heat was generated by mechanical work there was a constant equivalence between the amount of heat generated and the amount of work expended. Specifically, he measured the amount of mechanical work required to raise the temperature of water by a given amount and thereby established the mechanical equivalent of heat. A common expression for this equivalence is the Btu (British thermal unit), which is the amount of heat required to raise one pound of water by one degree Fahrenheit. The equivalent amount of mechanical energy is equal to 778 foot-pounds.

Second, it was learned that heat can be converted into mechanical energy only if in so doing the heat flows from a hotter body to a colder body. Thus, a heat reservoir cannot have its heat energy converted to mechanical energy unless its temperature is higher than that of its surroundings. To help illustrate this, let us consider the existence of two reservoirs each with the same amount of identical fluid, but at two different temperatures. Heat from the higher temperature reservoir can be converted into mechanical work, but in the process some of the heat energy must be given to the lower temperature reservoir where it cannot be converted to any other form of energy. In short, some of the thermal energy originally in the high-temperature reservoir cannot be converted to mechanical work. This energy is not lost or destroyed, it just cannot be converted into mechanical work. This then puts a limitation on the amount of total heat energy that can be converted into mechanical energy. The oceans, for example, contain an enormous quantity of internal energy, but this energy cannot be utilized without the availability of a colder reservoir. This situation is analogous to the use of water power for turning a mill wheel: the total amount of work depends on the amount of water that impinges on the wheel and on the height from which it falls. Without a height differential between water levels, the water will not flow and so the wheel cannot be made to turn. Similarly, without a temperature differential, heat will not flow of its own accord unless it is from a warmer to a colder body.

These two discoveries about the nature of heat were of such basic importance that they have been formulated as laws which serve as a foundation for the whole present structure of thermodynamics. They can be simply stated as follows:

*First Law of Thermodynamics:* When mechanical work is transformed into heat, or heat into work, the amount of work is always equivalent to the quantity of heat.

*Second Law of Thermodynamics:* It is impossible, by any self-sustaining process, for heat to be transferred from a colder to a hotter body.

The first law states that heat is a form of energy. This is actually another way of stating the principle of the conservation of energy, namely, "energy can neither be created nor destroyed, it can only be converted into another form." The second law does not contradict the equivalence of heat and mechanical energy, but it does put a limitation on the proportion of the one that can be converted into the other. An understanding of the fundamental meaning of these two laws might be simplified with the help of an analogy. A principle that resembles the First Law of Thermodynamics could be applied to the exchange of currency. The traveler who changes his dollars to marks, pounds, francs, or lire knows that (except for the minor cost of the transaction) his money's total value remains unaltered, even though it can take one or more of several forms. Similarly, an analogy to the second law might be found by the traveler who goes to Israel. He can obtain three Israeli pounds for every dollar for as many dollars as he wishes to convert. However, if he wishes to reconvert his pounds he can do so only up to a limit of one hundred dollars. The value of his funds has by no means depreciated and he can use them for many attractive purchases, but, because the Israeli Government wishes to limit the outflow of its currency, he cannot convert more than three hundred pounds back into the form of dollars.

However, we need to see how these two laws will govern the behavior of our genie. Thus, where the first law states that the genie is indestructible, even though he can take various forms, the second law states that once the genie comes out of the lamp, he can never get completely back inside again. These two laws will underlie all our subsequent discussions, but their applicability must be expressed in terms of certain specific thermodynamic quantities which characterize a thermodynamic system. For this reason it is now necessary to define what is meant by a thermodynamic system, to specify the useful thermodynamic quantities, and to then show how they are interrelated.

## THE EQUATION OF STATE

Figure 5 illustrates a typical thermodynamic system which consists of a cylinder containing some gas, such as air, and a piston that fits sufficiently well to prevent the gas from leaking out. The piston has weight and therefore it acts to move downward and compress the gas in the cylinder. As a result the gas is compressed to a pressure somewhat higher than that of the surrounding atmosphere outside the system. In order to describe its thermodynamic state we need the quantitative knowledge about four characteristics of the system: the pressure in the gas, the volume occupied by the gas, the quantity of gas, and its temperature. It is also necessary to know how these four quantities are related, not only when the system is in a state of equilibrium but also when the equilibrium is upset. A system is in full equilibrium when it is in both mechanical and thermal equilibrium. It is in mechanical equilibrium when all the forces acting on the system are balanced. In the case of our example, the downward force exerted by the piston's weight is equalized by the upward thrust of the gas pressure. It is in thermal equilibrium when the temperature of the gas, of the cylinder walls, and of the outside are all equal. Thus according to the Second Law of Thermodynamics, no heat will flow. Our system is therefore in both mechanical and thermal equilibrium. This tranquil state of affairs is represented in Figure 5 (a).

Let us now find out how this system behaves when it is thrown out of equilibrium. This is readily done by the injection of a quantity of heat into the gas. This heat injection will trigger the following sequence of events. First, the heat will raise the temperature of the gas and

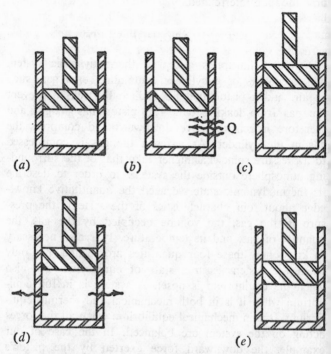

Fig. 5. Typical thermodynamic system: (a) Temperature of gas
in cylinder is same as surroundings. Pressure of gas in
cylinder is sufficient to equalize weight of piston. System is
therefore in thermal and mechanical equilibrium. (b)
Heat is injected into system. (c) Heat raises temperature
of gas and causes pressure to rise and lift piston. Gas in
piston is at higher temperature than surroundings so system is out of thermal equilibrium. (d) Heat flows from
higher to lower temperature, pressure is decreased, and
piston is lowered. (e) All injected heat has flowed out
and system is back in thermal and mechanical equilibrium.

thereby cause the gas pressure to increase. When this increased pressure acts on the piston it will overbalance the force exerted by its weight and the piston will be made to move upward. But, as the piston moves upward, the volume occupied by the gas will increase and so the pressure will begin to lower. Eventually the gas pressure will be lowered to the point where it is again exactly equalized by the downward thrust of the piston. The system has now returned to a state of mechanical equilibrium. However, it is not in a state of thermal equilibrium since the gas temperature is higher than that of the cylinder walls and of the outside atmosphere. Accordingly heat, which will always flow from a warmer to a cooler region, will start to flow into the walls and on out into the surroundings. As the heat flows out the pressure will drop further, and the weight of the piston will become greater than the resisting force; as a result, the piston will start to move down again. This process will then continue until all of the heat originally injected into the system has flowed back out and the entire system returns to its original state of equilibrium.

It should be noted that as the system changed from one state to another, that is from its initial state to a higher energy state caused by the injection of a quantity of heat, its behavior was at all times consistent with the two laws of thermodynamics. In its original state of equilibrium the system did have internal energy in the form of thermal energy stored in the gas, but since there was no temperature differential no heat flow was possible, as predicted by the second law. Action was possible only when a quantity of energy, $Q$, in the form of heat was injected into the system to unbalance its equilibrium. Although this heat was partially and temporarily converted into the mechanical energy necessary to lift the piston, to warm the cylinder walls, and eventually to be lost again

by flow through the walls, this energy was never destroye
but only changed in form.

While the unbalanced system was attempting to re
store its equilibrium, the following cause-effect relatior
ships were noted: the injection of a quantity of heat, C
caused the temperature, $T$, to go up; an increase in vo
ume, $V$, then caused the pressure to go down. Thes
cause-effect relationships, however, are not meaningf
unless they can be quantified, that is, unless it is possib
to determine by how many psi the pressure is increase
when the temperature is raised a certain number of de
grees and to know how much the pressure is decrease
by a given volume increase. Quantitative answers t
such questions are provided by a deceptively simple re
lationship which is the single most important relationshi
in interior ballistics—the Equation of State. The use c
this equation is fundamental to every application wher
gas is contained in a receptacle. For a perfect gas th
Equation of State is given simply as

$$P \cdot V = n \cdot R \cdot T$$

where $P$ is the pressure in the gas,

$V$ is the volume occupied by the gas,

$n$ is the quantity of gas,

$R$ is a quantity known as the Universal Ga
Constant,‡ and

$T$ is the gas temperature.

This equation is universally applicable to any gas.

Although the equation is extremely simple, it can't b
useful in a meaningful way until we have a better under
standing of the individual thermodynamic quantities tha
constitute this equation. It will also be necessary to es
tablish a measure for a quantity of heat which can caus
the state of a system to be altered. For this reason w

‡ The quantitative value of $R$ depends upon the system of unit
used, as will be shown on page 74.

will temporarily defer a discussion of the equation until these quantities are defined, such as $n$, representing the quantity of a gas, and $Q$, the quantity of heat. The quantity of gas is normally measured in moles, and heat in calories, or Btu's. It will therefore be necessary first to define precisely what is meant both qualitatively and quantitatively by moles and calories, or Btu's. Moreover, it will be necessary to define the three remaining quantities, $V$, $P$, and $T$ in consistent, quantitative terms. For this reason it will be helpful if we defer our definitions of these quantities and take time out to give a brief review of the two principal systems of measurement used in the world today, the English and the metric systems.

## THE TWO SYSTEMS OF MEASUREMENT

The peaceful exchange of goods in a marketplace requires that merchants and buyers agree on some fixed basis for weighing and measuring. This, in turn, requires the availability of reference standards against which the accepted units of mass and length can be compared. In early civilizations these were generally a set of stone or bronze weights, in the custody of an official, and a fixed length which corresponded to the dimensions of some specific object. A set of such standards would then form the basis for a system of weights and measures. There have been countless such systems, but the two principal ones in existence today are the English system, based on the pound and the yard, and the metric system, based on the kilogram and the meter.

The English-speaking world uses a system of weights and measures that has evolved from a variety of sources, some of which date back to the time of the Roman occupation of Britain. This system did not develop in either a systematic or rational manner. The commonly used units of length, for example, are related by the followir inconsistent sequence of multiples:

$$
\begin{array}{rcl}
12 \text{ inches} &=& 1 \text{ foot} \\
3 \text{ feet} &=& 1 \text{ yard} \\
5\tfrac{1}{2} \text{ yards} &=& 1 \text{ rod} \\
40 \text{ rods} &=& 1 \text{ furlong} \\
8 \text{ furlongs} &=& 1 \text{ mile}
\end{array}
$$

It is not known which of these units came first an served as the reference unit for the others. It could hav been the foot and, as the name suggests, its length ma have been based on the physical dimensions of some earl big-footed lord. Nevertheless, by the time of the Amer can Revolution, the English system was well developed but it suffered from a lack of uniformity and, as a resul the units used in Great Britain did not always correspon to those in the American colonies. Moreover, when th United States and Great Britain subsequently and inde pendently standardized their systems, some of this lac of uniformity persisted. In both countries, the pound an the yard are the basic standard units of mass and length and these are equivalent in both countries.¶ However, lack of correspondence still exists with a few familia measures which are compared in the following table.

|  |  | U.S.A. | Great Britain |
|---|---|---|---|
| Mass | 1 ton | = 2000 lbs | = 2240 lbs |
| Capacity (liquid) | 1 gallon | = 231 cu ins. | = 277.42 cu ins. |
|  |  | = 128 ounces | = 160 ounces |
| Capacity (dry) | 1 bushel | = 2150 cu ins. | = 2218 cu ins. |
|  |  | = 4 pecks | = 8 gallons |

Even in the U.S.A., there are three kinds of ounces There is the avoirdupois ounce, which is the commo

¶ The standard American yard happens to be about one-ten thousandth of an inch longer than the British yard.

everyday measure of mass that we know as one-sixteenth of a pound; there is the troy ounce, weighing 1.097 times as much as the avoirdupois ounce; and finally there is the fluid ounce, which is not a measure of mass but of capacity and is equal to one-sixteenth of a pint. The lack of adequate standardization that had existed for so many years naturally facilitated the creation of new measures which often developed from local usage. As a result, new units of weight and measure popped up like mushrooms all over the English-speaking world. Many have been standardized into the system although, for the most part, they are seldom used except in certain professions and regions. In fact, the great multiplicity of these existing measures could form the basis of a quiz game where the players are asked to give quantitative definitions of such units as gills, drams, scruples, links, or hogsheads.

By contrast, the metric system was developed in a systematic way and its units of length, mass, and capacity are interrelated in a very simple and logical manner. This rational and consistent system was first proposed to the French National Assembly in 1790, during the very midst of the turmoil and tumult of the French Revolution. Various unrelated systems were in use at the time and scientists felt a desperate need for a unified system to replace a chaotic situation. A first objective in setting up the new system was the selection of an unchangeable standard of length, based on some entity in nature, in a way similar to the selection of a unit of time based on the earth's revolution. For this purpose the distance from the North Pole to the Equator, along a great circle on the earth's surface, was chosen. The next step was to measure this distance. It was of course unfeasible to physically traverse a straight line all the way from the North Pole to the Equator, but it was possible to measure a portion of the distance. Accordingly, the commission appointed by the Assembly decided to measure one-tenth of this total distance (i.e., nine degrees of latitude) and chose two points along a constant longitude, one at Dunkirk and one near Barcelona. And so, in 1792, two scientists embarked on this unusual and hazardous task of measuring this meridian along a straight line. The measured length was then divided by one million, to give a standard unit of length, the meter, which became the basic unit for the whole metric system. All other units of length in the metric system differ from the meter only by factors of ten, as is shown in the following table of the commonly used units of length:

| | |
|---|---|
| One meter | = 39.37 inches |
| One thousand meters | = a kilometer = .621 miles |
| One-tenth of a meter | = a decimeter |
| One-hundredth of a meter | = a centimeter (cm.) |
| One-thousandth of a meter | = a millimeter (mm.) |
| One-millionth of a meter | = a micron |
| One-ten-billionth of a meter | = an angstrom unit |

The admirable thing about the system was the fact that the units of weight were tied in directly to the units of length. As a standard of volume, a cubic decimeter was chosen as the standard measure of capacity, and this became the liter. The choice of a unit of mass was now simple and logical. One liter of water became the standard unit of mass, the kilogram, also called simply the kilo. Since the kilogram is one thousand grams, the gram is similarly the mass of one cubic centimeter of water. Two other commonly used units of mass in the metric system are the metric ton, equal to the mass of a cubic meter of water, and the milligram, equal to a thousandth of one gram. In order to convert from the metric to the English system, or vice versa, the following conversion factors for the basic units of length, capacity, and mass are used:

| one meter | = | 1.0936 yards |
| .9144 meters | = | one yard |
| one liter | = | 1.0567 quarts |
| .9463 liters | = | one quart |
| one kilo | = | 2.2046 pounds |
| .4536 kilos | = | one pound |

In addition to standards of mass and length, a complete system of measurements requires two additional units: time and temperature. A universal and satisfactory measure of time is based on the day, £ which corresponds to one revolution of the earth. This is an excessively large unit of time for most purposes, but before Galileo had discovered the principle of the pendulum, it was not possible to make accurate measurements of much smaller intervals of time. Today, in both the English and metric systems, the standard unit of time is the second, defined as 1/86,400 day.

The development of suitable units of temperature was only slightly less straightforward than the selection of a time unit. Like time, we tend to think of temperature in terms of the method of its measurement and therefore we automatically think of the thermometer. The commonly familiar type contains a liquid, such as mercury or colored alcohol, which is hermetically sealed in a glass bulb attached to a thin tube. As the temperature of the bulb rises or falls, the fluid expands or contracts. Differences in temperature are indicated by reference marks which represent the different heights to which the liquid in the tube rises. Thermometers of this type were already well known in Florence during the seventeenth cen-

£ The length of the day has long been regarded as one of the great absolutes. However, it has little inconsistencies which irritate the scientists' mania for precision and so, in October 1964, a much more accurate "atomic" standard of time was adopted, based on the vibration frequency of the element cesium, which is 9,192,631,770 cycles per second.

tury and were characterized by the use of enameled beads for indicator marks on the tube. However, thermometers were never calibrated against any consistent reference marks until 1714, when Gabriel Fahrenheit first proposed that two fixed points be taken as absolute references. For the first point, he arbitrarily selected the lowest temperature at which water could be made to remain in a liquid state, which he established with the best available anti-freeze materials of the time, a mixture of snow and common salt. In this manner, he established the zero on his Fahrenheit scale. The temperature of a healthy man's blood was then selected as the upper point. He first divided this range into twelve equally spaced intervals, but subsequently increased the number of divisions, or degrees, to 96. A uniform basis for measuring temperature was greatly needed, and so his arrangement was quickly accepted. It became the first standardized system for calibrating a thermometer, and its popularity persists today. Thus, zero degrees on his Fahrenheit scale represents the lowest temperature at which he was then able to maintain water as a fluid (32 degrees below the normal freezing point of water). Techniques for obtaining human body temperature were not yet well developed, so the high point did not exactly correspond to true body temperature, which is normally 98.6 degrees on the Fahrenheit scale. Other scientists, including Fahrenheit himself, later felt that these two reference points could have been more judiciously chosen. There is no real logical relationship between the temperature of a man's blood and the lowest temperature at which water can be kept fluid. He was therefore in agreement with subsequent proposals that a more logical system should be based on reference points at the normal freezing point and at the normal boiling point of water, which occur at 32 degrees and 212 degrees on his scale. Such a scale was subsequently adopted, and since the distance between the two refer-

ence points was divided into 100 degrees, the new scale
was called the centigrade scale. It should be noted that
when a temperature is given, the proper scale should be
indicated (unless otherwise understood). Thus, 50°F
means 50 degrees on the Fahrenheit scale; and 20°C
means 20 degrees on the centigrade scale. The way in
which a few selected temperature levels are given on
these two temperature scales is shown in the following
table:

|  | Fahrenheit | Centigrade |
|---|---|---|
| Absolute zero | −460° | −273° |
| Oxygen freezes | −361° | −218° |
| Oxygen boils | −297° | −183° |
| Water freezes | 32° | 0° |
| A pleasant day | 68° | 20° |
| Water boils | 212° | 100° |

In thermodynamics, however, it is much more useful
for a temperature scale to be in absolute terms; that is,
so the zero on the scale corresponds to absolute zero.
The absolute scales that correspond to the Fahrenheit
and the centigrade scales are the Rankine and the Kelvin
scales. Thus, the addition of 460 degrees to a temperature on the Fahrenheit scale converts it to degrees Rankine, and the addition of 273 degrees to a temperature
on the centigrade scale converts it to degrees Kelvin.
Thus water boils at 492°R (Rankine) and at 273°K
(Kelvin). The Equation of State, for example, will always use one or the other of these absolute scales. For
reasons based more on usage than logic, the Fahrenheit
scale (and the Rankine scale) tend to be used in con-
junction with the English system of weights and measures, while the centigrade scale (and Kelvin scale) tend
to be used with the metric system.

Now that we have identified the English and metric
systems of weights and measures as well as their asso-

ciated temperature scales, we have a quantitative basis for defining two important thermodynamic quantities: the mole, which is a measure of a quantity of gas; and the calorie (or the Btu), which is a measure of a quantity of heat.

## MOLES, CALORIES, AND BTU'S

Almost immediately after a child begins to talk he learns to count. Later when he goes to school and becomes more skillful in the use of numbers, he learns to use other measures of quantity. He quickly becomes familiar with the practical measures of weight and so he learns to think of tons of coal or pounds of iron. Similarly, as he becomes adept with measures of capacity, he easily works out the arithmetic exercises which deal with bushels of wheat or gallons of water. As schoolchildren acquire proficiency in the uses of weight, capacity, and number, they also develop an intuitive feeling for selecting the appropriate measure to specify the quantity of a given substance. Thus they automatically think of measuring sugar by the pound, milk by the quart, or eggs by the dozen. However, the unusual circumstance sometimes arises for which they find it difficult to select a suitable measure. This can be illustrated with the help of a situation which frequently occurs in the one-room country schools that characterize the rural Midwest. Sometimes on a warm spring day, the open windows will admit unwelcome visitors from a neighboring hive. At this point the classroom tranquillity may be suddenly shattered by the startling announcement that "the room is full of bees." Although this warning certainly describes an alarming situation, it does not include a suitable measure of quantity. In order to describe this exciting episode with quantitative accuracy, it may be necessary to fumigate the schoolroom and sweep up the dead bees into a receptacle. The question now is "How does one measure a quantity of bees?" It seems awkward to measure them by the pound or by the quart. Counting the dead bees appears simple but, if they number in the hundreds or thousands, this measure may also appear as questionable as it is tedious.

For a long time, the chemists had a similar problem in attempting to specify a quantity of gas. Measures of weight did not seem appropriate, as we can easily imagine if we try to think of a pound of oxygen or of hydrogen. Measures of capacity, on the other hand, appear much more suitable since one can easily visualize a fixed volume of a gas, such as a cubic foot of air. For the chemist, though, this is not quite sufficient, for he knows that a cubic foot of air in Miami is not the same quantity as a cubic foot of air on Mount Everest, or in the Arctic. The volume of a fixed quantity of gas will vary with the pressure and the temperature, and thus a measure of capacity is no longer a simple measure, since it requires additional data in order to be specific. Moreover, under the temperature and pressure conditions normally found in guns, a simple measure of capacity would be as vague a quantitative measure as "a schoolroom full of bees." However, if we exclude weight and capacity, we are left with "counting," which at first appears to be an even more unacceptable measure of quantity for a gas.

The dilemma was resolved in 1811, when Amedeo Avogadro, an Italian physicist, announced his principle that equal volumes of all gases, at the same pressure and temperature, contain equal numbers of molecules. According to Avogadro, if one were to line up a number of bottles of identical volume and fill the first with hydrogen, the next with carbon dioxide, and the rest with various gases, each bottle would contain the same number of molecules (that is, if the bottles are capped so the gases don't escape). If the bottle containing carbon dioxide, which has a molecular weight of 44, contains the same number of molecules as the bottle of hydrogen, with a molecular weight of 2, the contents of the one bottle will therefore weigh twenty-two times as much as the contents of the other. Avogadro further determined that if his container were to have a capacity of 22.4 liters, and if this container were to be filled with any gas at standard atmospheric pressure and at 0°C, then the weight of this gas, in grams, would be numerically equal to its molecular weight. Accordingly, if this container is filled with hydrogen, the weight of gas in the container will equal 2 grams, since its molecular weight is 2. Similarly, if filled with carbon dioxide, the contents will weigh 44 grams. On the basis of these considerations, a logical measure for specifying a quantity of gas was developed. It is called the "gram molecular weight," or a "gram mole," and is more commonly referred to simply as a "mole." Since Avogadro established the fact that equal volumes of different gases at the same pressure and temperature contain the same number of molecules, and since he also determined the volume that would contain a weight of gas numerically equal in grams to its molecular weight, the natural question arises, "How many molecules are there in a mole?" The answer is 602 sextillion molecules, which can also be written:

$$\text{One mole} = 602,300,000,000,000,000,000,000$$
$$\text{molecules.}$$

This number, appropriately enough, is known as Avogadro's number, usually written as $6.023 \times 10^{23}$. At 0°C and at a pressure of one atmosphere, which is 14.7 pounds per square inch, one mole will fill up a volume equal to 22.4 liters. Since 22.4 liters is equal to 23.7 quarts, it is almost equivalent to six gallons. Thus, it is convenient to think of a mole of gas as the quantity that will fill six one-gallon jugs under standard atmospheric conditions.

In referring to what is properly called a gram molecular weight we have used the simpler and more commonly used term, mole. However, it should be noted that the pound mole is also a unit and is similarly defined. Since a pound contains 453.6 grams, the pound mole is this much larger than the gram mole. The term mole should therefore not be used without specifying whether it is a pound mole or a gram mole, although if it is obvious that either the English or the metric system is used, no confusion results by use of the term mole.

Now that we have defined our measure of a quantity of gas we can turn to a definition of the measure of the quantity of heat.

The word *calorie* is a familiar one that often plagues the conscience of those who love to eat. In this context it represents a given level of energy-producing value in food when oxidized in the body. Actually a calorie, in thermodynamics, is simply a unit of heat. Specifically, it is that quantity of heat that will raise one gram of water by one degree centigrade.§ A similar unit is the kilogram calorie, or large calorie, which is the quantity of heat necessary to raise one kilogram of water one degree centigrade. The calorie that worries the dieter is in reality equivalent, in energy, to the thermodynamic kilogram calorie, equal to 1000 small calories. In the English system the measure of heat is the Btu (British thermal unit), which is the amount of heat required to raise one pound of water 1°F. Since there are 454 grams in a pound and since each °C is equal to 1.8°F, it is simple to establish the fact that one Btu is equal to 252 calories.

With these definitions in mind, it is now possible to translate a given quantity of heat, as measured in calo-

§ The amount of heat necessary to raise a quantity of water by one degree will vary slightly depending upon the original temperature of the water. More precisely defined, a calorie is the quantity of heat necessary to raise one gram of water from 15°C to 16°C.

ries or Btu's, into a specific increase in the temperature of water. However, we also want to know the relationship between the amount of heat injected and the resulting temperature increase in a gas. For this we need the definition of a quantity known as the heat capacity, which is that quantity of heat required to increase the temperature of a system or substance one degree of temperature. If we use moles as a measure of the quantity of gas, then we use a molar heat capacity, which is the quantity of heat necessary to raise the temperature of one molecular weight of the substance one degree. Thus, in English units the molar heat capacity is the quantity of heat necessary to raise the pound mole one degree Fahrenheit and, similarly, in metric units the molar heat capacity is the heat necessary to raise the temperature of one gram molecular weight by one degree centigrade. For gases the heat capacity does not remain constant over all temperature ranges. As an example, the following table shows the molecular heat capacities for a few common gases at several temperature levels:

TABLE 3
GRAM MOLAR SPECIFIC HEATS AT CONSTANT PRESSURE

| Gas | 0°C | 100°C | 1000°C |
|-----|-----|-------|--------|
| CO | 6.93 | 7.05 | 8.13 |
| $CO_2$ | 8.46 | 9.96 | 13.71 |
| $H_2$ | 6.84 | 6.92 | 7.65 |
| $O_2$ | 5.82 | 7.02 | 8.48 |
| $N_2$ | 6.77 | 6.87 | 7.77 |

This table gives the number of calories needed to raise the temperature of one mole of the gas one degree centigrade. For example, it takes 6.93 calories to raise a mole of carbon monoxide one degree if the gas is originally at 0°C. Remembering that CO has a molecular weight of $12 + 16 = 28$, this says that one mole weighs 28 grams, and thus it takes almost seven calories to raise 28 grams one degree.

Now that we have defined measures for a quantity of gas and of a quantity of heat, together with a definition of heat capacity, we can proceed toward the last two as yet undefined variables in the Equation of State: pressure and velocity.

## THE CONCEPTS OF PRESSURE AND TEMPERATURE

Virtually everybody seems to understand what is meant by temperature and pressure. Temperature is a word that plays the leading role in mankind's universal topic of conversation, the weather. Pressure is another well-worked word whose use is frequent and whose meaning is assumed to be self-evident. Most people cannot articulate their own definitions of these words, but there is always ready access to the dictionary, which says that pressure is "a force in the nature of a thrust distributed over a surface" and that temperature is the "degree of hotness or coldness measured on a definite scale." These definitions are not wrong, but for our purposes they are inadequate. To understand the nature of pressure and temperature in thermodynamics, a somewhat more fundamental comprehension is needed. We will attempt an explanation here for which we will need two oddly dissimilar objects: a beam balance and a billiard table.

The arrangement illustrated at the top of Figure 6 shows an ordinary beam balance in equilibrium. A receptacle poised above the right-hand tray is full of very small steel ball bearings. In the next illustration the receptacle is tilted so that it pours a stream of these balls onto the tray. Each little ball immediately bounces off after impact so that the tray is never actually carrying

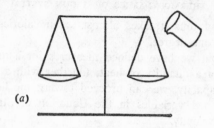

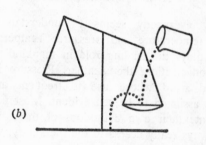

Fig. 6. The beam balance: (a) Beam balance is in equilibrium. Container poised above right-hand tray contains small ball bearings. (b) Container is tilted and a stream of ball bearings impinges on and bounces off tray. This causes balance to tilt. (c) Weight placed in left-hand tray exerts a downward force equal to that of stream and so balance is again in equilibrium.

any weight. Nevertheless, it is apparent that this stream of bearings will force the right-hand tray downward. Since the stream exerts a force on the tray we would naturally, and correctly, suppose that if a suitable weight is placed on the left-hand tray, as shown in the third figure, it can be made to equalize the effect of the stream. Similarly, if the receptacle is raised so that the individual steel balls drop from a greater height and therefore impact at a higher velocity, a larger weight will be needed to counterbalance the greater force exerted by the stream. The effective force of this stream can also be increased by either an increase in the rate at which the bearings flow out of the receptacle, or by an increase in the masses of the individual pellets. The important point to note here is that a stream of particles exerts a force against a surface on which it impinges. This force, moreover, depends on the mass of the individual particles, on their impact velocity, and on the rate at which they impinge. With this illustration in mind we temporarily shift the scene to a billiard table.

Figure 7 shows a large number of billiard balls on top of a billiard table. As every billiard player knows, a moving billiard ball quickly loses its velocity as a result of impacts with other balls and with the side cushions. This velocity loss occurs simply because the other balls and the cushions are not completely elastic, and a little of the ball's energy is lost after every impact. However, our billiard table is an idealized one where all the balls and the cushions are perfectly elastic. At a given signal a number of billiard players will step up to the table and each player will drive one of the balls in an arbitrarily chosen direction. As a result, the billiard balls will suddenly all be set in motion. They will then be continuously hitting each other and glancing off into more collisions both against the other balls and the cushions. Since the cushions and balls are completely elastic, the total

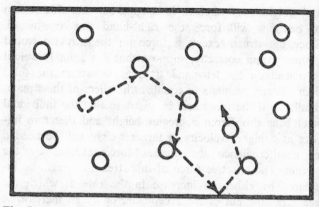

Fig. 7.

motion will not slow down. Any one of the individual balls in motion will change direction after each collision and will also lose or gain velocity depending on whether the collision is "head-on" or "tail-on." Although individual balls will be losing or gaining velocity after every impact, the total motion, that is, the average velocity of all the balls, will not change. The connection between the stream of bearings impinging on a beam balance, the motion of billiard balls on an idealized table, and the nature of pressure and temperature in a gas can now be made. The explanation for the connection is provided by the Kinetic Theory of Gases, a very useful theory developed during the latter half of the last century. This theory is based on the following assumptions about the nature of the molecules of a gas in a container:

1. All of the individual molecules of the gas are in continuous random motion (like the billiard balls).

2. The individual molecules behave like perfectly elastic spheres and are therefore continuously bouncing off other molecules and against the walls of their container. (Thus the motion of the molecules of gas is a three-

dimensional analogy of the motion on our big billiard table.)

3. The actual total volume occupied by the molecules themselves is negligible by comparison with the volume in which they are moving.

4. The molecules exert no other forces of attraction on each other (thus it is only their collisions with other molecules and walls that influence their behavior).

According to the Kinetic Theory of Gases, the total amount of motion in a container of gas will remain constant for a given temperature level. However, if a quantity of heat is added this will cause the individual molecules to move at a higher average velocity. It should be noted that as a given molecule zooms around colliding with the other molecules, it can lose velocity from "head-on" collisions and gain velocity from "tail-on" collisions. Thus the individual molecules, like the billiard balls, will be continuously changing velocity and direction. Yet, for a given quantity of gas in a given volume at a given temperature, the average velocity of all the molecules will remain constant. A notion of the magnitude of this molecular movement is shown in the following table, which gives the average velocity of the molecules, the mean distance each molecule travels before it collides with another molecule, and the average number of collisions per second. The data are shown for two different temperature levels at a standard atmospheric pressure level of 14.7 psi.

### TABLE 4

| Molecule | Average Velocity (meters/second) | | Mean Distance between Collisions (millionths of a centimeter) | | Average Number of Collisions per Second (in millions) |
|---|---|---|---|---|---|
| | at 0°C | at 20°C | at 0°C | at 20°C | at 20°C |
| Hydrogen, $H_2$ | 1696 | 1755 | 16.00 | 17.44 | 10,060 |
| Nitrogen, $N_2$ | 454 | 471 | 8.50 | 9.29 | 5070 |
| Oxygen, $O_2$ | 425 | 440 | 9.05 | 9.93 | 4430 |
| Carbon Dioxide, $CO_2$ | 362 | 376 | 5.56 | 6.15 | 6120 |

We can now talk about the pressure and temperature in a gas. The pressure exerted by the gas on the walls of a container is due simply to the collision of great numbers of molecules impinging on the walls in a way identical to that of the ball bearings impinging on the tray of a beam balance. Table 4 shows the molecular motion of several gases all at the same pressure level. The hydrogen molecules are much smaller and lighter than, say, the carbon dioxide molecules, but their mean velocity is higher and as a result the pressures caused by the impacts are in both cases equal to 14.7 psi.

To sum up, the temperature in the gas is really a measure of the average velocity of the molecules. Thus when heat is added to the container its net effect is to cause the average velocity of all the molecules to be increased. The pressure, on the other hand, is a measure of the frequency of collisions. This frequency can be increased by any of three ways: a decrease in the volume available to the gas; an increase of the quantity of gas (i.e., injecting more gas into the available volume); or an increase in the velocity of the gas molecules, which is equivalent to an increase in temperature.

## THE TRUE NATURE OF THE GENIE

Just before she awoke from her adventures in Wonderland, Alice, beset by the Queen of Hearts and her bizarre entourage, finally cried out, "You're nothing but a pack of cards." So might we recognize the genie of the propellant as nothing but zillions of infinitesimally small elastic particles in rapid random motion. Yet by the visualization of a gas in these terms, such concepts as quantity, temperature, and pressure take on a somewhat different but more useful meaning. For a given gas, enclosed in a fixed volume, the "quantity" of the gas, as measured in moles, is actually a measure of the number of gas molecules in the volume; the "temperature" is really a measure of the average velocity of the molecules, while the "pressure" is a measure of a frequency of collisions. These notions, derived from the Kinetic Theory of Gases, can now provide a basis for a meaningful understanding of the Equation of State, which as first given on page 54 is

$$P \cdot V = n \cdot R \cdot T$$

Before using this equation we need a value for the quantity $R$, which was defined as the Universal Gas Constant. This is very easily obtained from our definition of the gram mole (page 64), which stated that at 0°C and at a standard pressure of one atmosphere one gram mole would fill up a volume equal to 22.4 liters. In this one sentence we are given, for a particular state of a gas, its temperature $T$, its quantity $n$, its pressure $P$, and its volume $V$. Since we know four of the five quantities in the equation, it will be simple to find the value of the fifth. We can first tabulate the four known values and in so doing put them in consistent units; i.e., we will use kilograms, centimeters, and degrees Kelvin. In this system the four quantities take on the following values:

$P$, Pressure = 1.0333 kilos per square centimeter
    (= standard atmosphere = 14.7 psi)
$V$, Volume = 22,400 cubic centimeters
    (= 22.4 liters*)
$n$, Quantity of gas = 1 mole
$T$, Temperature = 273°K (0°C)

---

\* Even a system as simple and logical as the metric system becomes contaminated by minor inconsistencies. Actually, one liter = 1,000.027 cubic centimeters.

By the substitution of these values of $P$, $V$, $n$, and $T$ into the Equation of State we quickly find that

$$R = (P \cdot V)/(n \cdot T) = (1.0333)(22,400)/(1)(273)$$
$$= 84.8$$

This value of the gas constant, however, depends on the use of units based on kilograms, centimeters, and degrees Kelvin. For the four more commonly used combinations of units the value of the gas constant is given as follows:

for pounds, inches, degrees Rankine, $R = 18,510$
for pounds, feet, degrees Rankine, $R = 1543$
for kilos, centimeters, degrees Kelvin, $R = 84.8$
for kilos, meters, degrees Kelvin, $R = 848,000$

Now that all the quantities in the Equation of State for a perfect gas have been identified, we can easily manipulate the equation to obtain specific relationships for given values of the variables. However, it is more important to have a clear understanding of its physical meaning. To begin, we'll consider a fixed quantity of gas, $n_1$, in a closed container whose volume can be changed. In its initial state it has a volume of $V_1$, a pressure of $P_1$, and a temperature of $T_1$. This situation is represented by the point on the bottom curve in Figure 8($a$). If the temperature remains at $T_1$ and the quantity of gas $n_1$ remains fixed, then only the pressure and volume can change. A volume decrease causes the average distance between molecules to decrease. Since it is assumed that the temperature is not changed, the average velocity of the molecules will not change. However, the decrease in distance between molecules will increase their frequency of collision, and as a result the pressure will go up. Similarly, if the volume is increased, the average distance between molecules will increase and so their frequency of collision will decrease, which results in a corresponding decrease in pressure. The system, under the constraints

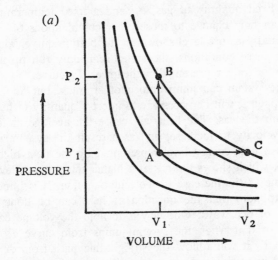

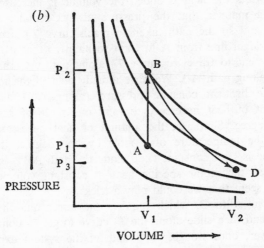

Fig. 8.

of a fixed quantity of gas, $n_1$, and a fixed temperature, $T_1$, can only change to those other combinations of volume and pressure level shown on the bottom curve. Thus, under these conditions, the system can only run up and down the track represented by the lower, $T_1$, curve.

The system can jump onto another track, but for this to happen it will be necessary to inject a quantity of heat, $Q$, into the gas. The heat will cause the average molecular velocity to increase, and as a result the system will go to a new energy level represented by the next higher curve, which shows the gas at a higher temperature level, $T_2$, due to the increase in molecular motion. It is important to note that the injection of heat can be done in either of two ways: One way is to hold the volume constant so that when the system jumps from curve $T_1$ to curve $T_2$ it will follow the straight-line path from A to B and in so doing the pressure will go up. In the second way, while the heat is added the volume is increased in such a manner that the pressure always remains constant, and so the path taken to reach curve $T_2$ is along the straight line from A to C. It so happens that it takes more heat to travel to curve $T_2$ along path AC than it does along path AB. We have already defined the molar specific heat at constant pressure (along AC) as the amount of heat necessary to raise one mole of gas by one degree. Similarly, the amount of heat necessary to raise the temperature of a mole by one degree, if the volume is kept constant (i.e., along the path AB), is defined as the molar specific heat at constant volume. It might seem that we could play a trick on the system and go from A to B, which requires the lesser quantity of heat, and then slide along the $T_2$ curve to get to point B. However, once we get to B and let the system expand by its own higher pressure, it will actually travel along the path BD, which takes it to a point below the $T_2$ curve. This is due to the fact that some of the heat which was used to raise the system to the temperature $T_2$ is converted into the work necessary to expand its volume. The important thing to remember is that it takes more heat to go from track $T_1$ to track $T_2$ by path AB than by path AC. Thus the specific heat at constant pressure is larger than the specific heat at constant volume. The ratio of the specific heats, which is the specific heat at constant pressure divided by the specific heat at constant volume, is a very useful quantity in thermodynamics. As examples of its value, for air at normal sea level conditions the ratio is about 1.40 while for hot propellant gases in guns its average value is approximately 1.25. At this point our discussions on thermodynamics come to a seemingly abrupt halt. Before these thermodynamic ideas can be developed any further it will be necessary to review some concepts in physics, which will be done in the next chapter. We will then come back in Chapter 5 to show how the Equation of State and the specified heats can give us a measure of the genie's power.

As this chapter closes, the scene shifts and finds us in a brief reverie. We are sitting in a moderate-size room, the doors and windows are closed, the air is still, and all is absolutely quiet. Yet we know the air cannot be still. There are skillions of molecules in very rapid motion colliding with us, with each other, and against the walls. Since they are in motion they have energy. The First Law of Thermodynamics tells us that the energy cannot be destroyed but only changed in form. As we will see in Chapter 5 there is an enormous quantity of internal energy in this quiet room, more than enough to throw a large automobile over a skyscraper. However, the Second Law then tells us that since the surroundings are all at the same temperature no heat can flow, and therefore this energy cannot be utilized. This reverie tells us a little about the difference between the genie of the lamp and the genie of the propellant. Aladdin's genie could pop in and out of the lamp at will, and so was not obeying the Second Law of Thermodynamics. This points up one difference between the real and the fanciful. The real world is governed by natural laws. Our understanding of this complex world, moreover, is made much easier if we appreciate and understand these laws.

# CHAPTER 4

# THE PHYSICS OF PROJECTILE MOVEMENT

"Round and round she goes and where she stops nobody knows." So chants the carnival pitchman as he turns the wheel of fortune. To the hopeful onlookers it truly seems that only fickle chance can decide "where she stops." Similarly, such events as a twirled roulette, a flipped coin, or a thrown pair of dice seem solely susceptible to random chance. The bouncing ball, dancing around the spinning roulette, the coin on its twisting trajectory, and the pair of dice scrambling across the green cloth take paths so complex that their outcome is virtually unpredictable. Yet, in every case, the movements of these objects are completely controlled and predetermined by certain laws of motion. In fact, any and all movement, from the fluttering fall of an autumn leaf to the endless orbits of the planets, must conform precisely to these laws. Thus for any object that is set in motion, its path, its eventual resting place, and its final attitude are predetermined by the characteristics and condition of the object itself, by the forces that propel it, and by the forces that resist its movement. The relationship between the forces that act on a body and its resulting movement is the theme of this third act of our drama.

In the second act we saw a genie convert himself from a granular propellant into a hot gaseous form and, because he did this within the constraint of a small volume, reacted with the exertion of enormous pressures. This third and last act will show how these pressures become accelerating forces which in turn act to move a projectile. The purpose of this chapter therefore is to explain, both qualitatively and quantitatively, how the enormous forces created by the genie act on the projectile, how they are opposed by the reactive forces of friction, and how they finally give the projectile its velocity. While all this takes place the total quantity of energy in the system, as required by the First Law of Thermodynamics, remains constant. Moreover, as its form changes rapidly from heat into the projectile's kinetic energy, the conversion itself must be consistent with the Second Law of Thermodynamics. Thus when the drama is over, the total amount of energy is unchanged, but its distribution will in part have become irreversibly altered.

The relationships between forces acting on a body and its resulting motion are part of the science called physics. To visualize the way the pressures in a gun become forces, and then understand how the conversion from force to motion takes place, we need a background of two parts: precise definitions of certain terms, such as force, momentum, and energy; and an understanding of Newton's three laws of motion. With this background we can then more easily appreciate the action leading up to the climax of our drama as the projectile shoots out of the muzzle.

## FORCE, MOMENTUM, AND ENERGY

A bored child looking out an apartment house window must occasionally wonder what would happen if one of the flower pots were to fall to the sidewalk. While he might speculate on the probable consternation of the passersby, a physicist would describe such an event accurately and quantitatively in the following way: "A one-pound mass dropped from a 64-foot-height will be given a constant downward acceleration by the force of gravity and as a result it will impact with a velocity of 64 feet per second, a momentum of 2 pound-seconds, and an impact energy of 64 foot-pounds." This description may seem confusing, and a little stuffy, but it can become easily clear once we establish the precise meaning of the six key words in the sentence: mass, velocity, acceleration, force, momentum, and energy. These words are part of our everyday vocabulary, but we normally use them in loose and somewhat ambiguous ways. In the language of physics, on the other hand, they each have a very specific meaning. Once the following definitions of these six terms are understood, the above sentence can be reread and much more easily comprehended.

*Mass:* The mass of a body is a measure of the total quantity of matter in the body. There is a tendency to use the term "mass" interchangeably with "weight." It is conventionally believed, for example, that if a specific body has a mass of one pound, it weighs one pound. This happens to be perfectly true, *on the earth's surface*. On the surface of the moon this same body will weigh only one-sixth of a pound and, if in deep space or in orbit, it will be weightless. Thus a body's weight will change depending on its location in the universe. Its mass, on the other hand, is an invariable characteristic that will not change. It should therefore be clear that the terms "mass" and "weight" are not synonymous. Mass is a measure of quantity of matter, while weight is a measure of the gravitational force acting on a body. This distinction will become more clear after the definition of force is understood.

*Velocity:* Velocity can be simply defined as the distance traveled by an object per unit time. It is commonly measured in feet per second, centimeters per second, or miles per hour. It must be understood, however, that the velocity of an object may not be constant, in which case it is necessary to specify the object's velocity at a given instant or at a given point. The one-pound mass has no velocity at the instant it is dropped, but when it is half-way to the ground it will have a velocity of 32 feet per second and will impact with a velocity of 64 feet per second.

*Acceleration:* Acceleration is the change in velocity per unit time. The one-pound mass traveling 64 feet to the ground will be continuously accelerated at a rate of 32 feet per second for every second of travel. It should be noted at this point that the acceleration of 32 ft/sec/sec is the downward acceleration* of a body falling to the earth, but on the moon this value is about one-sixth as much, or some 5.4 ft/sec/sec.

*Force:* If we lift a one-pound object we intuitively know that we must exert an upward force of one pound to just lift it. This means that we have to apply this force to compensate for the gravitational pull on the object. A lunar astronaut, however, would need only exert a one-sixth-pound force to barely lift it. This then suggests that the force acting on a body is proportional to *the mass of the body* times *the acceleration acting on the body*. Thus we can make the following statement: "A force of one pound acting on a body that has a mass of one pound will cause it to be accelerated 32 ft/sec/sec." We can also write this as a simple but extremely useful equation:

$$F = (M/g) \cdot A$$

where
$F$ = force in lbs
$M$ = mass in lbs
$g$ = 32 ft/sec$^2$

and
$A$ = acceleration in ft/sec/sec

At this point someone can properly object, "I have seen this formula written as $F = M \cdot A$ [without the $g$]." The

* The acceleration caused by gravity, $g$, at the earth's surface varies from 32.09 feet per second at the equator to 32.26 at the poles. For convenience in our discussion we round it to 32 feet per second.

reason is simple. To write this equation as $F = M \cdot A$ physicists use a different unit of mass called the slug, which was made to equal "$g$" lbs, i.e., 32 lbs. Therefore it should always be borne in mind that:

$$F = (M/g) \cdot A \quad \text{if mass is in lbs}$$
$$F = M \cdot A \quad \text{if mass is in slugs}$$

At this point we can help clarify the distinction between mass and weight. Mass, as mentioned previously, is a measure of the amount of something. Weight, on the other hand, is a measure of force. The need for this distinction has been caused in part by the fact that the word "pound" is used both as a unit of mass and a unit of force. Thus, a *mass* of one pound will also exert a downward *force* of one pound on the surface of the earth. The physicist at all times must make sure that the distinction between these uses of the same word is clearly implied.

Before continuing with the definitions of momentum and energy it will be helpful to point out that if an observer could make accurate measurement of the velocity of the falling flower pot at various times and distances, he could summarize the data in Table 5.

TABLE 5

| Time (seconds) | Distance of Fall (feet) | Velocity of Object (feet per second) |
|---|---|---|
| 0 | 0 | 0 |
| $\frac{1}{2}$ | 4 | 16 |
| 1 | 16 | 32 |
| $1\frac{1}{2}$ | 36 | 48 |
| 2 | 64 | 64 |

*Momentum:* A body's momentum is simply defined as the product of its velocity and its mass, or

$$\text{Momentum} = M \cdot V$$

If mass is given in slugs and velocity in feet per second, the momentum is given in pound-seconds. Table 5 shows that the flower pot weighing one pound will be traveling at 64 feet per second at the instant before it shatters on the sidewalk. Since the flower pot has a mass of one pound, and since a slug is 32 times greater than a pound, the flower pot has a mass of (1/32) slug. Hence its momentum is

$$(1/32) \ (64) = 2 \text{ lb-secs}$$

Momentum is the result of a force acting for a given period of time. Since the flower pot has a mass of one pound, the gravitational pull of the earth will exert a downward force on it equal to one pound. This force acting on the flower pot for two seconds, as seen from the table above, caused the 64-foot-per-second velocity. The product of force (one pound) and time (two seconds) gave the flower pot an impulse, $I$, which is equal to the momentum. Thus

$$(\text{force}) \cdot (\text{time}) = \text{impulse}$$
$$(\text{mass}) \cdot (\text{velocity}) = \text{momentum}$$

On the basis of Newton's second law it will be seen that

$$\text{momentum} = F \cdot t = M \cdot V$$

*Energy:* Energy can be defined as the capacity for doing work. Whereas the First Law of Thermodynamics states that energy can neither be destroyed nor created but only changed in form, we are now interested in only one of its forms,† mechanical energy. We can define mechanical energy in a somewhat backward manner by first defining a unit in which it is measured, the foot-pound. If a body has a mass of one pound, it will take

† The forms energy can take are seven in number: chemical energy, heat energy, mechanical energy, radiant energy, sound energy, electrical energy, and atomic energy.

one foot-pound of work to lift the body one foot. Similarly, it will take 64 foot-pounds to lift the body 64 feet. It therefore took 64 foot-pounds of work to take the flower pot 64 feet up to the apartment. These 64 foot-pounds were then stored in the pot as potential energy. When the pot was dropped, the potential energy was converted into the kinetic energy of the falling pot. A moving body's kinetic energy can be expressed either as the force exerted to accelerate the body times the distance over which it is accelerated, i.e.,

$$\text{energy} = (\text{force})\,\text{times}\,(\text{distance}) = F \cdot x$$

or as one-half of the body's mass times its velocity squared,

$$\text{energy} = (\text{half the mass})\,\text{times}\,(\text{velocity squared})$$
$$= (M/2)V^2$$

If the mass is measured in slugs, and velocity in feet per second, then the energy will also be given in foot-pounds. (This can be checked by referring to Table 5). Accordingly, we can say that

$$\text{energy} = E = F \cdot x = (M/2)V^2$$

With these six definitions well understood we can now proceed to a discussion of a subject that has preoccupied thinkers since earliest times—the nature of motion.

## THE LAWS OF MOTION

Man's unquenchable curiosity about the nature of his world has prompted an unceasing effort to understand the bewildering complexities of his physical environment. The ancients compensated for their imperfect comprehension with imaginative explanations that either imputed animate spirits to inanimate objects or attributed their movement to the unpredictable whims of the gods. Thus a stream would flow because its spirit so moved it, or a breeze might suddenly gust up because Aeolus, who kept the winds chained in an enormous cave, had unleashed one for some special errand. The early Greek philosophers, with their more rational outlook, sought for plausible physical explanations. Of all these, the one that was to prevail was based on the theory developed by Aristotle‡ (384–322 B.C.). He accepted the idea that all matters consisted of some combination of the four basic elements: earth, air, fire, and water. He then conceived of a fiery realm in the heavens, the true home of air and fire, and toward which these two elements were impelled to move. Similarly, earth and water were continually striving to reach their true terrestrial domain below. In this scheme of things, a flame rises because it seeks its true place above, while an apple falls because its more abundant elements, earth and water, must move downward to their natural region. This movement of a body toward its natural place was defined by Aristotle as natural motion. Conversely, unnatural motion represented that movement of a body in a direction contrary to its true nature. Force he then defined as the action necessary to cause a body to move in unnatural motion. A man would therefore need to exert force in order to lift a log or fling a stone.

Aristotle's theory was accepted because it was plausible, it was logically consistent, and it provided a rational

‡ Aristotle first developed the science of logic and invented the syllogism, which takes the following structural form:

Assumption:  All puppies are playful.
Fact:        Hector is a puppy.
Conclusion:  Hector is playful.

A conclusion is a logical one if it is obtained by the correct use of a set of logical steps. It can, at the same time, be untrue if an assumption or the assumptions are untrue. If Hector happens to have a morose nature, the above conclusion about his playfulness is logically correct but actually untrue, simply because the assumption (like most generalities) is not universally true.

explanation for the observable phenomena of motion. Moreover, with the passage of the centuries, the body of knowledge encompassed in Aristotle's writings was to become not only the final word but would be regarded as absolute and unquestionable truth. In fact, during the Dark Ages any challenge to the teachings of "the Master" met with severe disfavor. Consequently the Aristotelian Theory of Motion was to endure for two thousand years. There was also one other very good reason why this theory remained successfully unchallenged for so many centuries: no one could show that any of the underlying assumptions were incorrect. Moreover, since its logical structure was unassailable, the theory endured by virtue of the fact that it was not possible, at that time, to disprove it.

Nevertheless, since some of its assumptions were false, the Aristotelian theory could not be consistent with the actual nature of motion. One of the assumptions, for example, stated that a body's degree of natural motion must be proportional to the total quantity of the dominant substances in the body. One logical consequence of this assumption was the conclusion that if two similar bodies of different mass were to be dropped simultaneously from some height, the larger body would pick up more velocity and would therefore strike the ground ahead of the smaller one. In a celebrated series of experiments with bronze balls, Galileo demonstrated conclusively that this was not true. Thus by demonstrating that the logical conclusions of this theory were contradicted by the actual motion of bodies, Galileo proved that one or more of its assumptions must be false, and in so doing he shattered the whole structure of the Aristotelian Theory of Motion.

Galileo not only wrecked the Aristotelian theory but also succeeded in laying the groundwork for an accurate science of motion. His scientific approach, revolutionary for his time, was based on two premises: First, in making statements or hypotheses about nature, one must rely on observation and experiment and not on authority. His second premise was that natural phenomena, such as motion, can best be described by the language of mathematics. By applying his method to the problem of motion, he deduced that the earth exerts a gravitational force on a body which gives the body a constant downward acceleration. He then succeeded in measuring the magnitude of this gravitational acceleration. With the application of mathematical analysis to the physical problems of motion, Galileo derived formulas which described the movement of a falling body. (One of his formulas, the one that gives the distance, $D$, that a body will fall at the end of $t$ seconds, i.e., $D = (\frac{1}{2})gt^2$, was used in the preparation of Table 5.) After he developed his formulas for falling bodies, he applied them to the more complex problem of the motion of a projectile fired from a gun. By discounting the effect of air resistance, he was able to predict that the trajectory of a cannon ball was a parabola.¶ However, Galileo's great contributions did not necessarily earn him popularity. For his refutation of the Aristotelian theory he was thanked with scorn and derision. When he later developed evidence to prove the disquieting fact that the earth was not the center of the universe, and in fact revolved about the sun, he created contention, intensified the enmity of his colleagues, and aroused the dread wrath of the Inquisition. Nevertheless, in his own time he was appreciated by a learned few who completely accepted his revolutionary concepts of motion.

Among these learned few were such scientific luminaries as Huygens, Descartes, and Kepler, who were them-

---

¶ At this very time the course of history was being altered by the English naval gunners who had probably never heard of a parabola, or of Galileo, but were nevertheless looping long cannon shots with devastating accuracy into the Spanish Armada.

selves preoccupied with the nature of motion and who did much to advance more fundamental understanding of its true nature. The man that was to synthesize Galileo's and their work into a uniform, coherent system was Isaac Newton, who was born in 1642, the year Galileo died. The nature of motion, which had been explored and to a large extent established by Galileo, was formulated by Newton into three deceptively simple but truly profound statements. These are Newton's three laws of motion:

*First Law:* A body at rest, or in motion, will continue its state of rest or uniform motion (i.e., constant velocity) unless a force acts on the body to change that state.

*Second Law:* The acceleration of a body (i.e., its change of motion) is directly proportional to the force acting on the body and takes place in the direction of the straight line along which the force acts.

*Third Law:* To every action there is always an equal and opposite reaction.

The First Law, sometimes called Galileo's law, states that when all the forces acting on a body are balanced, there is no net unbalanced force and the body either remains at rest or continues to move in the same direction with constant velocity. The body is therefore in equilibrium. Accordingly, a body traveling at some velocity along a straight line would continue to do so indefinitely unless slowed down by forces of resistance or otherwise deflected by other forces. Thus a cannon ball, if not affected by the force of air resistance and the pull of gravity, would not describe a parabolic-like path, but would instead continue forever at its constant velocity along a straight line into the infinite depths of space. The Second Law defines force, by implication, as that agency which causes a body to be accelerated. This law effectively says that the acceleration on a body is proportional to the force and inversely proportional to the body's mass. It therefore also says that the force acting on a body is equal to the body's mass times the acceleration to which the body is accelerated, or

force = mass times acceleration

which in the shorthand of mathematics is written:

$$F = M \cdot A$$

The Third Law says essentially that if two bodies interact, the force exerted by the first body on the second body (called the action force) is equal in magnitude and opposite in direction to the force exerted by the second body on the first body (the reaction force). Imagine, for example, a swimmer who attempts to push a boat. He exerts a force with his arms, the action force, which causes the boat to move, but at the same time he also experiences a force, the reaction force acting on himself, that pushes him away from the boat. Thus, the action of his arms not only accelerates the boat forward but also accelerates him backward. These three laws provide the foundation for the whole science of motion.

Although much of what is expressed in the three laws was discovered by Galileo and partially known by others, it was Newton who developed and synthesized this knowledge into a unified, consistent, universally applicable theory. Newton not only observed, described, and formalized the nature of motion, he also discovered a fundamental principle that applies throughout the universe. He formulated this basic principle as his Law of Universal Gravity. According to this law, every physical body in the universe is attracted to every other body. £

£ This law states that any two bodies, with masses $M_1$ and $M_2$, attract each other with a force, $F$, proportional to the product of their masses and inversely proportional to the square of the distance, $R$, between them. It is therefore expressed by the formula:

This then means that not only do celestial bodies, like the sun and the planets, exert their enormous attractive forces, but even two apples sitting side by side on a dish will exert a mutual attractive force that may be infinitesimally small (about one-billionth of an ounce), but a force nevertheless.

## THREE SIMPLE FORMULAS

At first glance Newton's three laws of motion might seem no more than sensible statements. However, as we shall see presently, these laws form the necessary basis for deriving useful relationships about motion. A main purpose of this chapter, for example, is to establish a relationship between the violent pressure raised by our thermodynamic genie and the resulting motion of the projectile it hurls from the gun muzzle. In other words, we need to know how to translate gun pressures into orderly measures of a projectile's final velocity, its momentum and its energy; thus we will derive three very simple and useful formulas. All that is needed for their derivation are the definitions given earlier in the chapter and Newton's Second Law.

### 1. Determination of Velocity from Pressure

The first formula to be derived will predict the muzzle velocity of a projectile from the mean pressure§ in the gun tube. In its derivation it will be seen that the formula itself is simply a logical consequence of four statements:

---

$F = GM_1M_2/R^2$. If the masses $M_1$ and $M_2$ are measured in grams and the distance $R$ in meters, the value of the constant $G$ is .000666.

§ Actually the pressure in the tube does not remain constant, so it will be necessary to remember that we will be referring to a mean, or average, pressure. The conventional way to represent an average value is to place a bar over the symbol for the quantity. Accordingly, we will henceforth designate mean pressure as $\overline{P}$.

(a) The definition of acceleration
(b) Newton's Second Law
(c) The definition of pressure
(d) The relationship between pounds and slugs

The derivation proceeds as follows:

(a) *The definition of acceleration:* According to the definition, "Acceleration is the change in velocity per unit time." This statement can also be expressed mathematically as:

$$\text{acceleration} = (\text{velocity/time})$$

or
$$a = v/t$$

By means of a simple algebraic manipulation the statement can be rewritten as:

$$\text{velocity} = (\text{acceleration}) \text{ times} (\text{time})$$

or
$$v = a \cdot t \qquad (1)$$

In its altered form, $v = a \cdot t$, the relationship says that the velocity imparted to a body is a product of the acceleration acting on the body and of the time during which the acceleration acts.

(b) *Newton's Second Law of Motion:* The next step in the derivation is provided by Newton's Second Law which, as we have seen, says that

$$\text{force} = (\text{mass}) \text{ times} (\text{acceleration})$$

or
$$F = M \cdot a$$

This can also be rewritten as:

$$\text{acceleration} = a = F/M$$

By substituting this expression for acceleration, $a$, into the relationship $V = a \cdot t$, we obtain an altered form of equation (1),

$$v = F \cdot t/M \qquad (2)$$

(c) *The definition of pressure:* Pressure is force per unit area, or

$$\overline{P} = F/A$$

which can be rewritten as:

$$F = \overline{P} \cdot A$$

The substitution of this expression for $F$ into equation (2) changes that equation to

$$V = \overline{P} \cdot A \cdot t/M \qquad (3)$$

Note that since pressure, $P$, is a mean pressure it has been designated $\overline{P}$. Although formula (3) gives velocity as a function of pressure, it is still not in a convenient form since mass, $M$, is given in slugs. We therefore want to modify the formula to express mass in pounds, which is the unit in more common usage. To make this change we go to the last step in the derivation.

(d) *The relationship between pounds and slugs:* This simple relationship between mass in slugs, $M$, and mass in pounds, $m$, is given by

$$M = m/g$$

where $g$ is the gravitational constant. The substitution of $m/g$ for $M$ in formula (3) completes the derivation and gives, in directly useful terms, the desired formula for the final velocity of a body accelerated down a tube as a function of the mean pressure in the tube.

$$V = \overline{P}At(g/m) \qquad (4)$$

where $V$ = final velocity, in ft/sec

$\overline{P}$ = average pressure, acting on body, in lbs/in.$^2$

$A$ = cross-sectional area of tube, in in.$^2$

$t$ = time during which pressure acts, in seconds

$g$ = gravitational constant

$m$ = mass of the accelerated body in pounds

## 2. Determination of Momentum from Pressure

A formula which relates momentum to mean pressure is also easy to derive. It only requires the definitions of momentum and of pressure. The momentum, or impulse, $I$, was defined as the force acting on a body multiplied by the time during which the force acts, which can be written as:

$$\text{momentum} = (\text{force}) \text{ times} (\text{time})$$

or

$$I = F \cdot t$$

By again expressing the relationship between mean pressure and mean force as:

$$\bar{F} = \bar{P} \cdot A$$

and by then substituting this expression for force into the one for momentum, we obtain the desired formula for the momentum of a projectile as it leaves the muzzle.

$$I = \bar{P} \cdot A \cdot t$$

## 3. Determination of Energy from Pressure

By a similar and equally simple logic we can take the definition of energy as:

$$\text{energy} = (\text{force}) \text{ times} (\text{distance})$$

or

$$E = F \cdot X$$

and by again substituting the expression for $\bar{F} = \bar{P} \cdot A$, we obtain our third formula

$$E = \bar{P} \cdot A \cdot X$$

This gives the energy of a projectile leaving the muzzle as a function of mean pressure.

## 4. Summary of the Formulas

It should be remembered at this point that momentum was also defined as (mass) times (velocity)

or
$$I = M \cdot V*$$

Energy was also defined as

(half of the mass) times (velocity squared)

or
$$E = (M/2)V^2$$

For convenience these formulas should be modified by expressing mass in pounds instead of slugs, and thus by substituting $m/g$ for $M$. We can now summarize our formulas for velocity, momentum, and energy as follows:

velocity $\quad V = \bar{P} \cdot A \cdot t(g/m)$

momentum $\quad I = \bar{P} \cdot A \cdot t; \quad$ also $\quad I = (m/g) \cdot V$
$$= M \cdot V$$

energy $\quad E = \bar{P} \cdot A \cdot X; \quad$ also $\quad E = (m/2g)V^2$

## MOTION OF THE PROJECTILE

The easy utility of these three formulas is best illustrated by their actual applications to some specific examples. However, before proceeding it is first necessary to note that the formulas all use a fixed value for the pressure, which is the mean, or average pressure. Yet during the firing process in a gun the pressure is by no means a fixed value; it rises rapidly until it reaches a maximum value and then decays during the remainder of the time the projectile is in the bore. It is therefore necessary to establish a simple means for relating the actual pressure rise and fall to a value for the mean pressure in a gun.

Figure 9 shows how the pressure rises and falls during

* Remembering also from Newton's Second Law that $F = M \cdot a$, and from the definition of acceleration that $a = V / t$, it is easy to see that $F = M \cdot a = M \cdot V / t$, or $F \cdot t = M \cdot V$. Thus the Second Law shows why the two definitions of momentum: (force) times (time) and (mass) times (velocity) are the same.

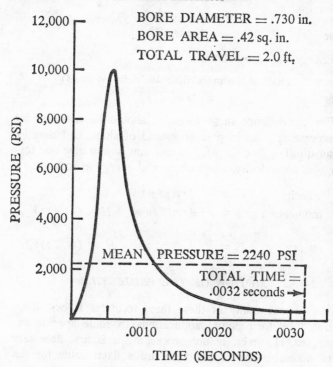

Fig. 9. Pressure-time curve for 1⅛-ounce shot shell load.

the time interval from propellant ignition to muzzle exit for a typical shotgun load. This load, used in the popular sport of breaking claybirds, contains 1¼ ounces of lead shot and is fired from a 12-gauge shotgun, which has a bore diameter of .730 inch. The solid curve that represents this pressure behavior is called a pressure-time curve.† The average pressure level is represented by the dotted horizontal line. Similarly, the dotted vertical line represents the magnitude of the time interval during which the shot charge was moving in the bore. These

† The measurement of pressure-time is discussed in Chapter 6.

two dotted lines, together with the two solid lines representing the pressure and time scales, enclose a rectangle. The value of the average pressure level is such that the area of this rectangle is equal to the total area under the pressure-time curve. Since the height of the rectangle is $\bar{P}$, the average pressure level, and its length is $t$, the total time interval, the area of the rectangle is simply equal to $\bar{P} \cdot t$. This is therefore the same as saying that the value of $\bar{P} \cdot t$ is equal to the area under the pressure-time curve.

We can now proceed to obtain the velocity, momentum, and energy for the load whose pressure-time characteristics are illustrated in Figure 9. The pertinent characteristics of this load are the following:

$$\bar{P} = 2240 \text{ psi (average pressure)}$$
$$t = .0032 \text{ sec (time interval)}$$
$$x = 2.0 \text{ ft (distance that the load}$$
$$\text{moves in the barrel)}$$
$$m = .077 \text{ lb (mass of lead shot and}$$
$$\text{of wads)}$$
$$A = .42 \text{ sq in. (area of bore)}$$

With these values the formulas can be used directly as follows:

$$\text{velocity} = \bar{P} \cdot A \cdot t \cdot g / m = \frac{(2240)(.42)(.0032)(32)}{(077)}$$
$$= 1251 \text{ ft/sec}$$

$$\text{momentum} = \bar{P} \cdot A \cdot t = (2240)(.42)(.0032)$$
$$= 3.01 \text{ lb-secs}$$

$$\text{energy} = \bar{P} \cdot A \cdot x = (2240)(.42)(2.0)$$
$$= 1882 \text{ ft-lbs}$$

## RECOIL MOTION OF THE GUN

So far the discussion has concerned itself with the motion of the projectile. Yet, while the propellant gases exert a forward accelerating force on the projectile, they simultaneously exert an equal accelerating force rearward on the gun. As a result the gun is also made to move. To a novice, discharging a firearm for the first time, this rearward movement is unexpected and so he is invariably startled by the gun's recoil. The magnitude of this recoil motion varies greatly from gun to gun. In the case of the caliber .22 rifle used in the shooting gallery, the recoil is almost imperceptible. On the other hand, for some heavy shotgun loads and for the type of guns and ammunition used in hunting very large game, the recoil can be uncomfortably heavy for an inexperienced shooter.

The reason for, and the magnitude of, this recoil motion is simply understandable and predictable from Newton's Third Law of Motion—"To every action there is always an equal and opposite reaction." The meaning of the Third Law is that the force accelerating the projectile forward is matched by an equal force accelerating the gun rearward. It is also easy to see that the lighter projectile will be given a much higher velocity than the heavier gun. In the previous section we saw how we could combine the definition of acceleration and Newton's Second Law to come up with the expression

$$V = F \cdot t / M$$

where     $V$ = velocity (of the accelerated body)
$F$ = the force acting to accelerate the body
$t$ = time during which force is acting on the body
$M$ = the body's mass

Let us now apply this formula to the two masses: the projectile mass, indicated as $M_1$, and the gun mass, designated $M_2$. Similarly, we designate the final projectile and gun velocity as $V_1$ and $V_2$ respectively. We can therefore write

$$V_1 = F_1 \cdot t_1 / M_1$$

and

$$V_2 = F_2 \cdot t_2 / M_2$$

Newton's Third Law states that the forces $F_1$ and $F_2$ are equal. The times $t_1$ and $t_2$ during which the forces act must also be the same. Therefore if

$$F_1 t_1 = F_2 t_2$$

we can readily conclude that

$$M_1 V_1 = M_2 V_2$$

This simple but all-important relationship permits us to find $V_2$, the velocity imparted to the gun, by rearranging the above relationship as

$$V_2 = (M_1 / M_2) \cdot V_1$$

This relationship‡ simply states that the gun's recoil velocity is equal to the ratio of the projectile to the gun mass times the projectile velocity. As an example, let us suppose that we are firing a projectile weighing 140 grains (or .02 lb, since one pound equals 7000 grains) at a velocity of 3200 ft/sec in a gun that weighs 6.4 lbs. The velocity of the gun is given by the above formula or

$$V_2 = (.02/6.4)3200$$
$$= 10 \text{ ft/sec}$$

‡ It should be noted that the relationship above does not take into account the momentum of the propellant gases as they rush out. For high-velocity projectiles that use a comparatively heavy propellant charge, the motion of the propellant gases can increase the recoil motion by as much as 100 per cent.

According to Newton's First Law the gun would continue this rearward velocity indefinitely unless another force acts to change it. This force is provided by the shooter's shoulder, which reacts to the sudden rearward movement of the gun with a decelerating force which quickly brings the gun's movement to a halt.

## THE FINAL TRANSFORMATION
## OF THE GENIE

The drama comes to its climax in the final scene as the hot high-pressure gases propel a projectile out the muzzle. At this point it will be useful to give a brief review of the actor and his performance, which he completed during an interval so brief that it is measured in thousandths of a second. Our principal performer was a genie named nitrocellulose whose origins were in a boll of cotton where he began as cellulose. Given enormous power by a potion of nitric acid, tranquilized and given self-control by diphenylamine, he was finally changed from a fibrous form to a hard plastic-like consistency after an association with a solvent. Cut to proper geometry and loaded in a cartridge, he was then ready for the instant of action. Once the ignition process was initiated the transformation from a solid to a gas began taking place on the surface of each granule of propellant. During this chemical decomposition the nitrocellulose molecules disengaged themselves and formed smaller molecules of gas, which immediately flew away from the surface at very high velocities. When the surface layer was transformed, the process continued onto the next layer, and then onto subsequent layers so that the propellant-burning process very much resembled the way a log burns from the outside in.

As a result of the transformation of nitrocellulose, myriads of molecules in rapid random motion collide with each other, with the barrel walls, and with the base of the projectile. In a way analogous to the pouring of shot onto a scale, the bombardment of these molecules exerts a force against the walls and the projectile. The resulting force on the base of the projectile is greater than its resistance, so the projectile begins to move. With every subsequent collision some momentum from the colliding molecule is imparted to the projectile, and it is thus accelerated. Yet for every increment of momentum given to the projectile, an equivalent amount of momentum is lost to the gas molecules, and as a result their mean velocity decreases. At the same time the movement of the projectile increases the volume which the gases can occupy, and this in turn causes the frequency of collisions to be reduced; thus the gas temperatures and pressures are lowered. When the projectile leaves the muzzle, the genie who has now been completely transformed into high-velocity gas molecules rushes out the muzzle to be forever dispersed.

Although nitrocellulose has been the big actor, the real theme of this action is energy. It is therefore just as important to review the way energy has altered in form from chemical to thermal to mechanical during the infinitesimally brief interval from ignition to muzzle exit. A good example of this energy transformation is provided by the shot shell whose pressure-time curve was shown in Figure 9.

Figure 10 shows the total distribution of energy in its three forms, chemical, thermal, and mechanical, throughout the .0032-second interval. As the figure shows, the energy at the beginning is all chemical energy, stored in the unfired propellant. At the end of one millisecond, about 40 per cent of the propellant remains unburned, while the remaining 60 per cent has been converted into thermal energy stored in the hot gases. Yet, about 20 per cent of the total energy has also been converted from thermal energy to the mechanical energy of motion. It is important to note here that some of the thermal energy is given directly to the barrel. As the molecules collide against the barrel wall, they lose some of their momentum, which is given to the steel molecules which begin to vibrate. This vibration then manifests itself as heat in the barrel.

The distribution of energy at the instant of muzzle exit can be determined roughly as follows: The particular shot shell load is charged with 21 grains of propellant of a type whose effective energy content is approximately 1,400,000 foot-pounds per pound. If one pound equals

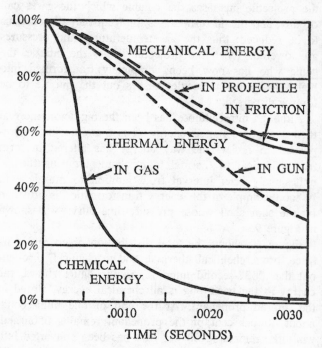

Fig. 10. Total energy distribution throughout time interval that projectile is in gun for 1⅛-ounce shot shell load.

7000 grains, then 21 grains is equal to .03 lb. This means the total chemical energy content in this load is

$$(.03)(1,400,000) = 4200 \text{ ft-lbs}$$

However, from page 97, we calculated the total kinetic energy of the projectile and wads at the instant of muzzle exit to be 1882 foot-pounds. This represents the total amount of energy converted to mechanical energy. About 25 per cent of the total propellant energy converted to heat was in turn absorbed by the barrel walls. Almost all the remaining energy, at the instant of muzzle exit, was still in the form of thermal energy stored in the hot gases. The final breakdown is given in the following table:

TABLE 6
FINAL ENERGY BREAKDOWN

| | | | |
|---|---|---|---|
| *Mechanical energy* | To projectile | 1782 = | 42.4% |
| | Friction | 100 = | 2.4 |
| *Thermal energy* | In hot gases | 1218 = | 29.0 |
| | In barrel wall | 1050 = | 25.0 |
| *Chemical energy* | In unburned propellant | 50 = | 1.2 |
| | Total | 4200 | |
| | | ft-lbs = | 100.0% |

It should be noted that of the 1882 foot-pounds converted to mechanical energy, some 100 foot-pounds were necessary to overcome friction and thus were taken away from the useful energy of the projectile. There is also a small fraction of the propellant that was never burned, which in this case amounted to slightly more than 1 per cent. (This propellant was actually burned, but its burning was not completed until after the projectile left the muzzle and thus did not participate in the reaction during the interval that the projectile was being accelerated in the barrel.) Although we are only interested in what takes place up to the instant of projectile departure, it should also be noted that further energy conversions will take place after the projectile leaves the gun. The thermal energy stored in the heated barrel will be converted to radiant energy given off by the barrel as it cools. Also, a very small fraction of the energy in the propellant gases will be converted into sonic energy which manifests itself as a healthy "bang."

The above breakdown of energy is consistent with the First Law of Thermodynamics, which says that energy will not be destroyed but merely changed in form. It is also consistent with the Second Law, which says that the bulk of the heat energy discharged as hot propellant gases into the atmosphere is not recoverable. Whereas the laws of thermodynamics state the nondestructibility of energy and impose limitations on its conversion, Newton's laws of motion, in turn, specify the way the projectile moves and thus describe the rate at which thermal energy is converted to mechanical energy throughout the total time interval.

CHAPTER 5

# THE PROBLEMS OF BALLISTICS

The Sphinx, a legendary winged human-headed lion, forced every man it confronted to guess the riddle: "What is it that is four-footed, two-footed, and three-footed?"* Those unfortunates who failed to answer correctly were immediately devoured. Riddles can be found wherever there are complex phenomena that are not easily susceptible to explanation. Even in interior ballistics there are questions which at first may appear to have all the baffling enigmatic attributes of a riddle. Incorrect answers to these questions, moreover, can also lead to disastrous consequences for the ballistics experimenter. The inability to answer the following three questions, for example, can result in a shattered barrel, a broken shoulder, or a gun that behaves unpredictably and inefficiently.

1. How can the incorrect choice of size and geometry of propellant granules cause a gun to blow up?
2. Why does an increase in projectile weight cause an increase in recoil discomfort even though the propellant charge is unaltered?
3. What is the maximum velocity a gun can give a projectile?

Although posed as riddles, these three questions exemplify the three principal problems in interior ballistics: to keep the pressures in a gun from ever becoming large enough to shatter it; to keep the recoil energy low

* The answer is Man, who first crawls, then stands on two feet, and in old age leans on a cane. According to the legend, when Oedipus gave the correct answer, the enraged Sphinx destroyed itself.

enough so that the shooter does not feel discomfort; and to obtain prechosen velocity levels with reliability and a reasonable degree of efficiency. The purpose of this chapter therefore is to discuss and deal with each of these three principal problems of interior ballistics. As is shown in the next three sections of this chapter, the answer to the first question is provided by the Equation of State, the answer to the second by Newton's Third Law of Motion, and the answer to the third question is obtained in part from the First Law of Thermodynamics. The chapter ends with the discussion of an additional question, which is related to the others, on the distinction between propellants and explosives.

## THE PEAK PRESSURE PROBLEM

The analogy between a propellant's energy conversion and a three-act drama was made deliberately in order to emphasize the three phases of the interior ballistics process: chemical, thermodynamic, and physical. By breaking the process down into these three steps the progression was seemingly an orderly one, as the chemical energy was changed to thermal and then in part to the mechanical energy of a high-velocity projectile. Yet it should also be remembered that every time a gun is fired a violent explosion takes place inside the gun, that enormous pressures are exerted against the barrel walls, and that the force unleashed by the explosion distends the cartridge case, strains the locking mechanism, and sets up shock waves in the metal that agitate the barrel into vibration. The peak pressure problem in interior ballistics is to make sure that these forces are never great enough to deform or burst a barrel. In order to understand the nature of the peak pressure problem it must be viewed from the standpoint of the gun's elastic properties and of its behavior when subjected to high pres-

## Plate 1

Evolution of the Gun.

Photographs courtesy of Winchester Gun Museum,
Olin Mathieson Chemical Corporation.

FOUR BARRELED EARLY HAND CANNON—1450

MATCHLOCK—ABOUT 1630

Plate 2

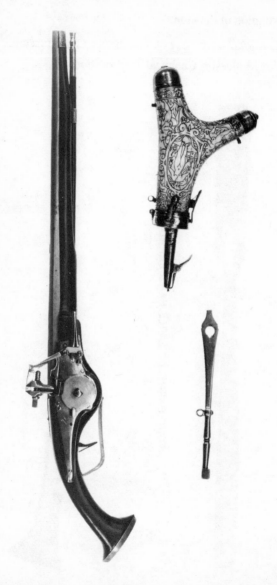

WHEEL LOCK CAVALRY PISTOL WITH KEY AND POWDER FLASK—1630

Plate 3

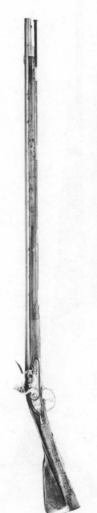

BRITISH "Brown Bess" FLINTLOCK—1733

SHARPS PERCUSSION LOCK—1859

Plate 4

WINCHESTER MODEL 73—"THE GUN THAT WON THE WEST"—1878

WINCHESTER MODEL 70—1961

# Plate 5

## Firing a Musket.

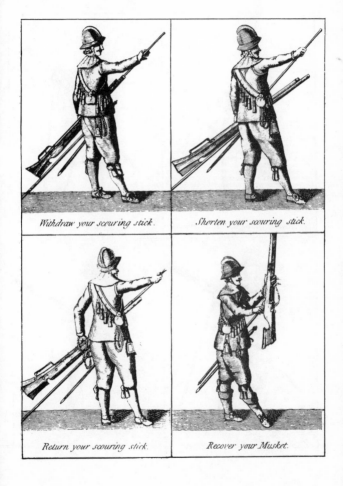

*Withdraw your scouring stick.*

*Shorten your scouring stick.*

*Return your scouring stick.*

*Recover your Musket.*

# Plate 6

## Firing a Musket.

Poize your Musket and recover your Rest.

Rest your Musket.

Blow your match.

Cock your match.

sures. The characteristics of a gun barrel's elasticity can be visualized with the help of a popular and very elastic denizen of the zoo.

A python, without provision for chewing, can devour a whole pig in one joyless gulp. As this enormous meal is worked back to his stomach, somewhat like a baseball forced through a rubber hose, it seems as if the snake would burst. The python, however, is an elastic reptile and as a result suffers no ill effects other than a sudden drowsiness. A similar thing occurs as a bullet travels down the bore of a gun. The pressures cause the barrel to swell, and as the bullet passes this swelling subsides. The steel gun tube, like the snake's gullet, is elastic, and if not stretched beyond suitable limits will rebound back to its original configuration. The characteristics of elasticity are illustrated with the help of Figure 11. Illustration (a) shows a normal everyday spring suspended from a fixed position, both before, during, and after a weight is attached. The weight causes the spring to stretch, and when it is removed the spring returns to its original configuration. Illustration (b) shows what happens if the weight is too large. In this case the spring will not completely rebound to its original length after the weight is removed. The spring is therefore said to have taken a permanent "set," which means it has been permanently deformed because of the excess force to which it was subjected. The final illustration shows what happens if the weight becomes really excessive. In this case the spring cannot even support the weight and will break. Python gullets, springs, and steel gun barrels are all elastic; i.e., they conform to Hooke's Law,† which states that for elastic bodies the amount of distension or deflection is directly proportional to the applied force.

† Named after Robert Hooke, 1635–1703, a cantankerous scientific genius who, had it not been for Isaac Newton, might have himself discovered the Law of Universal Gravitation.

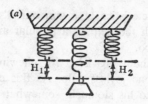

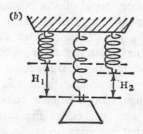

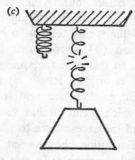

Fig. 11. Characteristics of elasticity: (a) When a weight is attached to the spring it will deflect a distance $H_1$. When weight is removed spring will rebound a distance $H_2$. If $H_1$ and $H_2$ are equal, the spring has rebounded to its original configuration. (b) Attachment of a heavier weight causes a larger deflection $H_1$. When weight is removed spring rebounds a distance $H_2$ smaller $H_1$. Difference between $H_1$ and $H_2$ is measure of permanent deformation to spring. (c) Excessively large weight causes spring to break.

This now brings up the question of the magnitude of the elastic limits of gun barrels. These depend on the barrel's dimensions, but for barrels used in typical small arms rifles pressures of 80,000 psi or over can cause permanent deformations, while pressures over 150,000 psi can cause ruptures. In practice, cartridges are loaded well below the levels that will cause any deformation, and thus in typical high-powered rifles peak pressures are held to about 50,000 psi. If this pressure level then defines the limits under which pressures must be kept, we turn to the Equation of State to determine what constraints must be placed on the propellant-burning process.

If we choose the English system of measurement and express the various terms of the Equation of State in pounds, inches, and degrees Rankine, the gas constant, as indicated on page 74, will be equal to 18,510. Our Equation of State then becomes

$$P \cdot V = n(18,510)T$$

However, in this relationship $n$ is given in pound-moles. Remembering that a pound-mole is the number of pounds of gas equal to the molecular weight of the gas, we can divide the quantity by this average molecular weight to express the quantity in pounds instead of in pound-moles. For a typical propellant the average molecular weight of the gaseous products of combustion is 24.1. Dividing this into 18,510 gives us 768 as the gas constant for our Equation of State if we measure the quantity $n$ in pounds instead of in pound-moles. At this point it should also be indicated that the temperature at which a propellant burns is approximately 6000°R (or 5540°F). This then gives the value of $T$ to be used in the Equation of State for the burning of propellant.

Let us now consider a gun system in which the initial volume occupied by the propellant is one cubic inch. It so happens that the weight of a cubic inch of propellant is approximately .057 lb. However, when it is in granular form and poured into a cartridge, one cubic inch will weigh approximately .036 lb, or about 250 grains. If this propellant were to burn completely in one cubic inch, the Equation of State says that

$$P \cdot V = n \cdot R \cdot T$$
or
$$P \cdot (1) = (1/28)(768)(6000)$$

This gives a value of the pressure, $P$, equal to 164,571 psi.‡ What this says in effect is that if the cubic inch were the filled volume of cartridge case, all of the propellant cannot be permitted to burn before the projectile moves. Thus, it is a fundamental necessity for the projectile to move an appreciable distance while the propellant is still burning. This situation is represented graphically in Figure 12. If the projectile, for example, moves enough so that the total volume behind it is four cubic inches, then, by substituting the value 4 for $V$ in the Equation of State we find that the pressure is equal to 41,142 psi (using the corrected form of the Equation of State the pressure level is found to be about 43,000 psi). Similarly, if the volume were to be increased to 8 inches, the simple form of the Equation of State gives a pressure level of 20,007 (where the corrected form gives about 22,000 psi). This all indicates the need for the projectile to move a sufficient distance to provide more volume. Since propellants burn at a fixed rate depending on the

‡ The actual value of the pressure obtained under these circumstances is much higher. We have used a simplified version of the Equation of State. A more exact relationship at high pressures is given by $P(V - Cb) = C \cdot R \cdot T$ where $C$ is the weight of propellant in pounds and $b$ is the "covolume" i.e., the actual volume occupied by the gas molecules. For propellant gases it is 26.3in.$^3$/lb. In this corrected form the pressure turns out to be greater than one million psi. For pressure levels below 20,000 psi the simplified form is reasonably accurate.

pressure level, and since they will burn more quickly if they are smaller in size, then the geometry of the propellant becomes acutely important in determining the peak pressure that will be obtained in the system.

Going back to the question, "How can the incorrect choice of size and geometry of propellant granules cause a gun to blow up?," it is apparent that if the granules are too small for the particular application the propellant

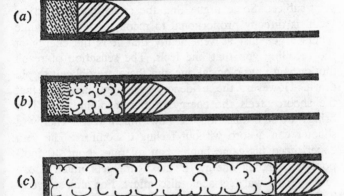

Fig. 12. (a) If all the propellant were to be converted into gas before the bullet moved, the resulting pressure would blow up the gun. (b) Bullet must move an appreciable distance while propellant is burning in order to provide enough volume to keep pressures from being excessive. (c) All of propellant cannot be burned until enough volume exists behind bullet.

will all burn too rapidly and pressures well over the safety limits can easily occur. For this reason the choice of propellant geometry is a very critical one and requires a trained ballistician.

## THE RECOIL PROBLEM

Our second riddle was "Why does an increase in projectile weight cause an increase in recoil discomfort even though the propellant charge is unaltered?" The answer is obtained from Newton's Third Law. However, the problem of recoil discomfort should first be discussed. One of the more popular arguments that invariably pop up when a group of shooters get together concerns this very subject. Some argue that the sensation induced by recoil is directly proportional to recoil momentum, while others argue just as vehemently that it is the energy of the recoiling gun that one feels. The sensation of recoil motion is a physiological one and therefore difficult to pin down. However, the evidence seemingly indicates that the shooter feels the energy of the recoiling gun. This brings up the question of how much recoil energy a shooter can absorb without feeling discomfort. The very experienced big-game hunter can tolerate about 40 foot-pounds of recoil energy. If the figure gets much above this level he will feel acute discomfort. For almost everybody else the upper limit of comfort is about 25 foot-pounds. The majority of rifles and shotguns have a recoil energy below a very comfortable 15 foot-pounds. With this in mind we can now consider Newton's Third Law to establish how a gun's recoil energy can be determined.

If we let $m$ and $v$ represent the mass and velocity of a projectile, and $M$ and $V$ represent the mass and velocity of a gun from which the projectile is fired, we obtain the familiar relationship

$$M \cdot V = m \cdot v$$

or

$$V = (m/M)v$$

We then have

$$\text{recoil energy} = (M/2)V^2$$

By substituting the value of $V$ we obtain the recoil energy as equal to

$$(M/2)(m/M)^2v^2 = (m/M)(m/2)v^2$$

This states that the recoil energy of the gun is equal to the recoil energy of the projectile multiplied by the ratio of projectile mass to gun mass. This little formula gives us the answer to the riddle. We know that if the efficiency remains reasonably constant the projectile energy will be proportional to the total propellant charge. The important factor here is the ratio $m/M$. It says that recoil energy can be increased by simply increasing the bullet weight, and can be decreased by increasing the weight of the gun. Thus if the recoil energy of a gun-ammunition system comes marginally high it can be reduced by increasing the gun weight, by decreasing the bullet weight, or by decreasing the propellant charge.

## THE MAXIMUM VELOCITY PROBLEM AND GUN EFFICIENCIES

The answer to the third question, "What is the maximum velocity a gun can give a projectile?," depends on how much of the propellant's energy can be converted into the energy of projectile motion. This in turn depends on two things:

(a) the total energy content of the propellant

(b) the proportion of this energy that can be converted into mechanical energy

In texts on thermodynamics it can be shown, by methods beyond the scope of this book, that if a cylinder fitted with a piston encloses a quantity of gas, the maximum possible energy given to the piston by the expansion of the gas is

$$E_m = PV/(k-1)¶$$

where    $P$ = the initial pressure in the cylinder
         $V$ = the initial volume in the cylinder
         $k$ = the ratios of specific heats

Remember from the discussion earlier in the chapter that if the Equation of State is expressed in pounds, inches, and degrees Rankine, then the value of the gas constant $R$ is 768. Hence for one pound of propellant (that will convert into one pound of gas), the value $PV$ is given by

$$PV = n \cdot R \cdot T = (1)(768)(6000) = 4,608,000$$

Remembering also, from page 77, that the ratio of specific heats, $k$, for propellant gases is about 1.25, we have

$$E_m = PV/(k-1) = (4,608,000)/(.25)$$
$$= 18,432,000 \text{ in.-lbs}$$

The energy is in inch-pounds simply because our units were pounds and inches. To convert to foot-pounds we merely divide by 12; so the theoretical energy content of one pound of propellant is

$$E_m = 18,432,000/12 = 1,536,000 \text{ ft-lbs}$$

This figure, however, is for a typical double-base propellant and does not take into account other constituents. A fraction of the weight of the propellant, as actually manufactured, is made up of such things as residual solvent, coatings such as graphite, and very often a deter-

¶ This is the idealized theoretical maximum and can occur only if the cylinder is infinitely long, if there is no gas leakage around the piston, if there is no frictional forces acting to impede the piston's movement, and if there is no pressure acting on the other side of the piston (which can only occur if the system were in a vacuum). If these conditions could be met then the total energy in the gas, which is in the form of energy of motion of the individual gas molecules, would be given to the piston.

rent material together with other minor ingredients which reduce the actual energy content per pound of most propellants to values from 1,200,000 up to 1,450,000 foot-pounds per pound.

At this point we can go back to a statement made at the very end of Chapter 3, to the effect that there is enough internal energy in a moderate-size room to throw a large automobile over a skyscraper. That statement can now be explained with a little calculation, using the formula for energy content. Let us assume that the dimensions of this room are a 10-foot height, a 10-foot width, and a 20-foot length. This gives it a volume of 2000 cubic feet. The normal atmospheric pressure is 14.7 pounds per square inch, or 2107 pounds per square foot (we want all our dimensions in feet and pounds). We also remember that the ratio of specific heats for normal air is 1.40. Our formula then tells us that the energy content in the room is

$$\text{(energy content)} = (PV)/(k-1)$$
$$= (2117)(2000)/(1.4-1)$$

which gives a value of more than 10 million foot-pounds. If the automobile weighs 5000 pounds then 10 million foot-pounds is enough energy to lift this automobile 200 feet.

Now that the total energy content of a propellant has been determined, we turn next to the question of what proportion of this energy can be converted into mechanical energy. As shown at the end of Chapter 4, the final breakdown of energy showed only slightly more than 40 per cent given to the shot shell pellet load. There are three factors which influence the proportion of heat energy convertible to projectile energy, and each of these will be discussed in turn:

1. The expansion ratio (also called the volume ratio)
2. Heat losses
3. The pressure gradient

Let us consider a cylinder whose total volume is $V_2$. A piston inside this cylinder encloses a gas at high pressure whose volume is $V_1$. The gas pressure will accelerate the piston until it is driven from the cylinder. If again there are no friction or heat losses, it can be shown in texts on thermodynamics that the total mechanical energy given to the piston is

$$E_m[1 - (V_1/V_2)^{k-1}]$$

The term $E_m$ is the energy content in the gas, while the term in brackets is the proportion of this energy given to the piston as mechanical energy. If $V_2$ is infinitely large, then the term in brackets is equal to one. However, for finite values of practical interest it is definitely less than one. The ratio of $V_2$ to $V_1$ is known as the volume ratio, and the value of the term in brackets as a function of the volume ratio is shown in the following table:

TABLE 7

| $(V_2/V_1)$ Volume Ratio | Percentage of Heat Energy Converted to Mechanical Energy of Piston |
|---|---|
| 2 | 15.9% |
| 4 | 29.3 |
| 6 | 36.1 |
| 8 | 40.5 |
| 10 | 43.8 |
| 20 | 52.7 |
| 30 | 57.3 |
| 40 | 60.2 |
| 50 | 62.3 |

In small rifles, depending on the caliber and cartridge size, the volume ratios (we can call this either the volume ratio or the expansion ratio) can vary anywhere from 5 to 20, although the greater majority are less than 10. Guns that use high-velocity cartridges tend to have lower volume ratios because the volume occupied by the propellant in the cartridge case, $V_1$, must be large if a large charge of propellant is to be used; hence the ratio of $V_2$ (the total volume in the gun) to $V_1$ becomes low. Thus as the propellant charge increases, the volume ratio will decrease and therefore, as shown in Table 7, the percentage of propellant energy that can be converted into projectile energy decreases. One answer to this is to increase $V_2$ by increasing the barrel length. However, barrel length cannot be increased much farther before a rifle becomes unwieldy. £ This then means that for a small arms rifle the maximum expansion ratio feasible will permit no more than about 50 per cent of the propellant energy to be converted into projectile energy.

The second source of lessened efficiency of a gun is the loss of heat from the propellant gases to the barrel walls. As shown in the final energy breakdown of a shot shell load discussed in the last chapter, 25 per cent of the total propellant energy ended up as heat in the barrel wall. The percentage is generally this high in shotguns. In the case of rifles, where the total time from ignition to projectile exit is much shorter and where the total metal surface area is less (small arms rifles have smaller bore diameters than shotguns), the proportion of propellant energy lost as heat transferred to the barrel walls is much less, generally about 10 per cent.

The third cause for the lessened efficiency of a gun as

£ In artillery pieces an increase in length is more feasible.

a heat engine is the "pressure gradient." After the projectile has begun its movement the propellant is still burning and adding fresh gases to the system. The pressure at the base of the projectile will be lower than that in the chamber, because it takes time for the pressure change in the chamber to be "transmitted" to the projectile's location. The nature of this pressure gradient problem is very complex, but from empirical measurements the following approximate relationship gives the ratio of pressure at the bullet base to pressure in the chamber:

$$\text{pressure ratio} = 1 - Cz/2m$$

where  $C$  is the mass of the propellant charge

$z$  is the proportion of the propellant that has been burned

and   $m$  is the mass of the projectile

Let us suppose we have 70 grains of propellant accelerating a 150-grain projectile, and let us further suppose that the propellant is 80 per cent burned. The formula then says that the ratio of pressure at the base of the bullet to the pressure in the chamber is

$$\text{ratio} = 1 - (60)(.8)/2(150)$$
$$= 1 - .48/(300) \qquad = .84$$

This says that only 84 per cent of the force that should be acting on the projectile is actually giving it its acceleration. It is quickly apparent that in the early portion of travel the proportion of burned propellant is low and thus the pressure gradient is very slight. However, as the projectile nears the muzzle and all the propellant is burned this pressure gradient can be appreciable.

These three factors, the volume ratio, the heat losses to the barrel wall, and the pressure gradient, all combine to reduce the efficiency of a gun. Whereas the shotgun gave an efficiency of slightly more than 40 per cent (as shown in the table at the end of Chapter 4), rifles have efficiencies that vary from 30 per cent to 40 per cent. Again, what is meant by efficiency here is the so-called thermodynamic efficiency, which is the proportion of propellant energy converted into the energy of projectile motion. Moreover, as attempts are made to increase the velocity level by increasing the propellant charge, the efficiency goes down. As a result it is very difficult to obtain velocity levels over 4500 feet per second. Above this level other problems of duplicability and reliability pop up and make the gun system unacceptably unpredictable. Thus the answer to our third riddle is, "Less than 5000 feet per second."§

## PROPELLANTS AND EXPLOSIVES

Heretofore the terms propellants and explosives have been used in a somewhat loose manner. It now becomes important to give them correct definitions. To begin let it be understood that all propellants belong to that family of materials we call explosives. The converse is not true, however, since some explosives are not propellants. By definition an explosive is a material which can be made to give off a great deal of heat, and generally a large volume of gas, very suddenly. The chemical decomposition of an explosive can take place in any of two fundamentally different ways: explosive burning and detonation.

*Explosive Burning:* In this process the reaction con-

§ This answer needs to be qualified. In some experimental systems where a long barrel is used together with a very light projectile and other special modifications, higher velocities can be obtained. However, for a conventional portable gun the above answer holds.

sists of the rapid ignition of successive layers of propellant. The gases generated, however, must be confined
to ensure continuation of the explosive burning process.*
The rate of this reaction is directly dependent on the
degree of confinement (or the pressure level). At typical
pressure levels, the burning rate is several inches per
second and the total burning time, in guns, may vary
from a fraction of a millisecond to several milliseconds.

*Detonation:* In this process, no confinement is necessary, as the rate of reaction is so rapid the high-pressure
gases do not have a chance to move away from the propellant surface. Initiation results from a shock wave
traveling through the material at thousands of feet per
second. As this shock wave moves through the material,
its instantaneous pressure causes decomposition. Explosives that decompose in this manner are called high explosives.

This difference in rate of reaction is of very great
importance to the internal ballistician since it determines
whether it is to be in inches per second or in thousands
of feet per second. The distinction separates explosives
into two classes: propellants and high explosives. High
explosives, such as TNT, picric acid, or nitroglycerin, cannot be used as propellants because of their excessive decomposition rates. Moreover, their decomposition is accompanied by very high-pressure shock waves which
could shatter most structures. Our concern will therefore
be with that class of explosives that can be classified as
propellants.

The critical properties of a propellant, in addition to
its energy content, are its burning rate and the geometry
of its individual granules. The combination of these two

---

* If a gun propellant were dumped out of a cartridge into an
ashtray and ignited, the propellant would flash up and burn vigorously like chips of wood soaked in gasoline, but this burning would
not in any way resemble an explosion.

properties establishes the so-called "quickness" of a propellant, which is a useful index for the specific type of gun in which the propellant is to be used. Burn rate, as the name implies, specifically refers to the rate of propellant decomposition. This chemical decomposition of a propellant granule begins at the instant the temperature on its surface reaches a certain level, which is characteristic for that particular propellant and which is defined as its ignition temperature.† The subsequent combustion of the granule progresses evenly from the outside surface where ignition occurs through subsequent layers of the propellant as each such layer reaches the ignition temperature. A propellant burn rate is a measure of the rate at which these layers burn. The burning rate depends upon the pressure and increases as the pressure is increased. During the burning action the hot gases generated during the combustion of one layer move rapidly away from the surface. If the pressure is too low, that is, if the degree of confinement is too low, flame contact with the propellant surface is low and the reaction stops. The burn rate is also influenced by the chemical composition, and generally increases with the percentage of nitroglycerin in the propellant. The following table gives the burning rate in inches per second for a typical small arms propellant:

TABLE 8

| Pressure Level | Burn Rate (inches per second) |
| --- | --- |
| 500 | .52 |
| 1000 | .75 |
| 2000 | 1.10 |
| 5000 | 1.70 |
| 10,000 | 2.25 |
| 20,000 | 3.55 |

† Nitrocellulose will ignite at approximately 300°C, but this ignition temperature varies greatly with various factors.

Propellant powders are made in a variety of sizes and shapes. Their range in size runs from the caliber .22 gallery cartridge, which uses granules smaller than grains of sand, to the 16-inch naval cannon that employs cylinders almost an inch in diameter and about $2\frac{1}{2}$ inches long. There are various shapes of propellant grains, of which the basic types are the following:

(a) Cylinders, with one or more perforations running completely through the grain from end to end.

(b) Cords, ribbons, flakes, or flat grains that can be diamond-, square-, or hexagon-shaped.

(c) Spheres, such as ball powder, and the shapes that result from the rolling and flattening of spheres.

Since the burning process proceeds evenly from the whole outside surface, a large, thin flake, or a long, single, tubular grain burning simultaneously from the inside and outside will present a near-constant surface area during burning. A cylinder or sphere, on the other hand, burning from the outside has a constantly decreasing surface. Such grains are commonly said to have the property of "regressive" burning. Conversely, a "progressive" burning grain is one whose burning surface increases during burning. For example, a perforated cylindrical, or tubular grain which has its outside coated with an inhibitor material, will burn from the inside out. Its burning surface area, accordingly, continually increases. For some given application the optimum performance is obtained by the employment of a carefully planned combination of burning rate and geometry. This also helps determine the total burning time, which is directly related to the burn rate and the minimum dimension of the grain.

This now takes us to a definition of the term "quickness" or "relative quickness." The term is sometimes loosely used to describe the rate of pressure rise of various propellants. Its more exact meaning refers to the time it takes the propellant to burn completely. It is used mainly in the evaluation of small-arms ammunition propellants and is determined experimentally. The quickness of a propellant is really a measure of how long it will take the granules to burn when confined in a gun. The quickness must be such that the projectile has moved a sufficient distance down the bore so that enough volume is available to prevent the pressure level from exceeding its maximum permissible value. In a small arms rifle this necessary distance of movement can be less than an inch for the smaller caliber, a couple of inches for the larger calibers, and a few feet for the large naval guns. If the propellant burns too slowly the burning process may stop; if it burns too rapidly the pressures become excessive.

Of all the problems of ballistics the question of a suitable choice of propellant geometry and burn rate, and thus of "quickness," is perhaps the most critical. Millions of shooters fire guns every year without an accident. Yet a few accidents do occur, and these are invariably traceable to the home experimenter, or hand loader, who has not been sufficiently careful to follow all the precautions necessary to ensure a proper choice of propellant quickness. If there were a Sphinx to query the experimenter as to what was the proper choice of geometry and burn rate, the unfortunate who could not answer would be liable to have a shattered gun and an injury.

# CHAPTER 6

# BALLISTIC MEASUREMENTS

The fundamental objective in the development of a physical science is to establish laws which govern the behavior of those events about which the science is concerned. This development can generally be divided into three phases. The first phase is devoted to the observation, or measurement, of empirical events. In interior ballistics, for example, this phase encompasses the measurement of such things as pressures and velocities inside a gun. During the second phase, these measurements are analyzed and synthesized to explain the observed phenomena in the light of available knowledge and, finally, to establish general laws. In the third and last phase, these general laws are tested and verified. To do this, the scientist first uses the laws to predict behavior under new or different conditions, which he contrives, and then he takes measurements to assess the accuracy of his predictions. It is apparent that the critical factor in the first and third phases is measurement for, without the means for making quantitative observations, the second-phase activity is necessarily constrained to fanciful speculations. Thus, measurement has become the powerful, indispensable instrument of the physical sciences. This is particularly true in an experimental science like ballistics, and the history of its growth as a science is almost identically the history of the development of methods for making accurate measurements.

The first ballistic measurement was probably made by a curious gunner who wanted to find out how far his piece would shoot. It was a fairly easy measurement, for all he had to do was pace off the distance to the impact point of his farthest shot. In the early history of firearms, this simple determination of total projectile travel, or range, suffered from an excessive variability caused by the very crudeness of the guns, the erratic quality of gunpowder, and the unsophisticated nature of the measurement. However, by the seventeenth century, as gunpowder and the various types of guns were improved and had become somewhat more reliable, the principal armies had measured and tabulated the maximum ranges for various popular kinds of artillery pieces with a reasonable degree of accuracy. These early ballistic range tables, which related shot weight, propellant charge, and gun elevation to extreme range, represent the first collections of tabulated ballistic observations. Attempts had also been made, ever since the early days, to estimate the destructive energy of a projectile by observing, for example, the number of planks it could smash through, or the depth to which it would embed itself in a tree. Such measurements might be helpful in making qualitative comparisons between the killing power of two artillery pieces, but they did not give quantitative measurements in any units that had a useful physical meaning. Gunners, moreover, didn't feel a particular need for them. They generally used the largest practicable charge of gunpowder and were then content if they knew their gun could shatter a mast, tear a hole in a ship's hull, or hammer down a wall. On the other hand, since measurements which related the range of a gun to its angle of elevation were of great practical utility, a gunner had to know how to adjust the elevation of his piece to hit a distant target. For the first four centuries in the history of guns, these range measurements were the only meaningful quantitative ballistic measurements that could be made.

The range of a projectile, however, is an exterior ballistic characteristic and reveals nothing about interior ballistic phenomena. Since no interior ballistic measurements were possible during all this time, essentially nothing was known about what took place inside a gun. This lack of knowledge did not seem to inhibit the development of guns for, by the eighteenth century, hundreds of thousands of men had been armed with reliable muskets or pistols and the cannon had become the most powerful force developed by man. Yet, this had all taken place with only the roughest quantitative estimates of the two most important interior ballistic properties: the muzzle exit velocity of the shot and the peak pressure in the gun. The first phase in the development of interior ballistics as a science could not begin until these two quantities could be measured. Adequate measurements of muzzle velocity were first made just over two centuries ago, and then a suitable technique for the measurement of maximum pressure in a gun was finally developed in the 1860s. During the latter part of the last century, the availability of pressure and velocity measurements, supplemented with a sufficiency of knowledge in chemistry, thermodynamics, and physics, made possible the beginning of the second phase in the growth of interior ballistics. This second phase culminated near the turn of the century with the establishment of laws, in the form of equations, which interrelate the pressure, the projectile's position and velocity, and the gas temperature at any instant of time until muzzle exit. Subsequent development in ballistic instrumentation, particularly since World War II, now enable the ballistician to obtain accurately measured magnitudes of virtually all meaningful interior ballistic phenomena. These new and improved measuring techniques, together with present-day computer facilities, have carried interior ballistics through its third stage and brought it to the full stature of a sophisticated physical science.

An adequate treatment of ballistic instrumentation is beyond the scope of this volume. Nevertheless, the subject matter of interior ballistics can be better understood and appreciated by a little familiarity with the ballistician's tools. The purpose of this chapter is to give a brief description of the methods currently used to obtain the more useful and commonly employed interior ballistic measurements.

## THE MEASUREMENT OF VELOCITY

The measurement of projectile velocity has been accomplished by two principal types of instruments: the ballistic pendulum, which actually measures a projectile's momentum; and the ballistic chronograph, which measures the time it takes a projectile to travel a fixed distance between two reference points. The ballistic pendulum was first used in 1742, and for almost a century and a half it remained the only available means for the measurement of projectile velocity. The electromagnet led to the development of the first ballistic chronograph in 1874, and the subsequent advent of electronics made possible the modern ballistic chronograph, which can measure short time intervals to within a few millionths of a second. The measurement of projectile velocity has been dominated by these two devices: the ballistic pendulum and the ballistic chronograph.

## 1. The Ballistic Pendulum

A principal preoccupation of the early experimenters was the search for a reliable means of measuring the velocity of a cannon ball. Some had actually tried to clock the time it took to traverse a given distance, but were frustrated by the inadequacy of their timepieces and by their inability to clock the passage of an object they could not even see. They were therefore compelled to find an alternate means for measuring velocity. Such a means was first provided by Galileo, who was able to show that if a body is launched vertically upward, its initial velocity can be estimated from the relationship:

$$\text{vertical launch velocity, } V = \sqrt{2gh}$$

where $g$ is the gravitational constant and $h$ is the observed height to which the body will rise. Thus, if a body is thrown upward and the height to which it rises can be measured, then its initial velocity is immediately determinable. Unfortunately, the ballisticians of Galileo's time were still no better off with this little formula, since a cannon ball fired vertically not only went out of sight, but its return was uncomfortably unpredictable. Consequently, the relationship could not be used for the direct measurement of a projectile's velocity. The practical utility of this relationship was therefore necessarily limited to conveniently measurable heights. Preferably the height should be less than 10 feet, and certainly less than 100 feet. Yet, if the value of $h$ is 100 feet, the corresponding value of $V$ is only 80 feet per second.* Nevertheless, this formula was to provide the key for the measurement of projectile velocity.

The clue to its use was discovered in Newton's Third Law of Motion. One logical consequence of the Third Law is that if a small moving body impacts against, embeds itself in, and gives motion to a stationary body, then the momentum (mass times velocity) of the moving body before impact is equal to the momentum of the large body after impact. If we designate the weight and velocity of the small body by $w$ and $v$, respectively, and those of the larger body by $W$ and $V$, then:

$$wv = WV\dagger$$

* If we take $g = 32$ feet per second per second, the above formula becomes $V = \sqrt{64h} = 8\sqrt{h}$. If $h = 100$ feet, then $V = 80$ feet per second.

† This is the same relationship that covers recoil motion, as shown in Chapter 4.

The meaning of this is made readily apparent by a simple example. Suppose we have a bucket of wet sand hanging from a tree. If a small bullet is fired into this bucket, the bullet will give the bucket a forward velocity. Let us also assume, for purposes of illustration, that the bullet weighs .01 pound, and has a velocity of 1000 feet per second. If the bucket weighs 5 pounds, then the above formula says that:

$$(.01)(1000) = 5V$$
or
$$10 = 5V$$

The value of $V$ is therefore 2, which means that the bucket was given a velocity of 2 feet per second. Thus, according to Newton's Third Law, all the momentum of the bullet is given to the bucket. The bucket of sand weighs 500 times as much as the bullet, and so the bucket is given a velocity that is 1/500 that of the bullet. The important point is that the high velocity of a projectile can be accurately converted, by a known factor, into the much lower velocity of a secondary mass.

The basis for velocity measurement can now be easily established and can be illustrated with the help of the contrivance shown in Figure 13. A firmly braced gun is shown pointed vertically at a stout keg supported a short distance above it. This keg is filled with anything that will make it heavy enough to contain the fired projectile and keep it from passing through the keg. On impact, the projectile imparts its motion to the keg, which is observed to rise a distance $h$. From Galileo's formula, this distance $h$ can be converted into the initial upward velocity of the keg. If this keg velocity is then multiplied by the ratio of keg weight to projectile weight, the projectile velocity is found. A formula that relates the projectile velocity directly to the height $h$ can be derived with simple algebra.

If the projectile weighs $w$ pounds, if its velocity is $v$ feet per second, if the keg (with the projectile in it) weighs $W$ pounds, and if it has an initial velocity of $V$ feet per second, then, from Newton's equivalence of momentum:

$$wv = WV$$

which can be written     $v = (W/w)V$

Also, from Galileo's formula:

$$V = \sqrt{2gh}$$

By combining these two relationships, we obtain:

$$v = (W/w)\sqrt{2gh}$$

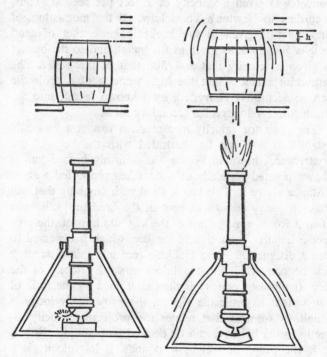

Fig. 13. Basis for velocity measurement.

If the keg weight, $W$, and the projectile weight, $w$, as well as the value of $g$ are known, then all that is needed is an observed value of the height, $h$, to which the keg rises in order for $v$ to be determined. To help illustrate the use of this simple formula, suppose the projectile weight, $w$, is one pound, and the keg weight, $W$ (with the projectile in it), is 250 pounds. Also, for arithmetic convenience, we will round the value of the gravitational constant, $g$, and assume it is equal to 32. We can now rewrite:

$$v = W/w\sqrt{2gh} = (250/1)\sqrt{64h} = 2000\sqrt{h}$$

If, for example, the keg is observed to rise one-quarter foot, then the projectile velocity is found to equal:

$$v = 2000\sqrt{\tfrac{1}{4}} = 1000 \text{ feet per second}$$

An arrangement such as the one shown in Figure 13 is, of course, completely impractical. Even if an observer, at his peril, were to stand close enough to measure the height to which the keg would rise, the smoke would make any meaningful observation impossible. Moreover, if the keg were heavy enough to contain the shot, it would rise but a few inches and this would lead to gross percentage errors in the visual estimation of the height $h$. This overall problem, however, was completely obviated, thanks again to observations that had been made by Galileo. He could also show that if a body at the end of a pendulum were given a lateral velocity $V$, then the absolute height $h$, to which this body would rise above the horizontal, could be given by his same formula:

$$V = \sqrt{2gh}$$

What this means is that the formula covers the two situations illustrated below. If a body at rest is given a vertical upward velocity $V$, it will rise a distance $h$. If, on the other hand, the body were suspended at the end of a pendulum and then given the same velocity $V$, which in this case is imparted laterally, the body will travel a longer path, but will reach the same absolute vertical height $h$ This is illustrated in Figure 14.

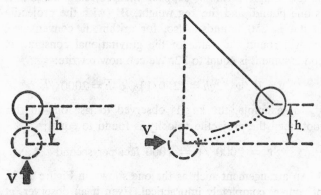

Fig. 14.

Benjamin Robins, a British mathematician, was the first to appreciate that a projectile's momentum could be measured by imparting it to a large mass suspended on a pendulum. His ballistic pendulum, first used in 1742, is shown in Figure 15. Here the shot is fired horizontally into a large wooden mass suspended on movable arms. As the shot imparts its motion, the mass swings in a long arc and carries along with it a sliding pointer that moves along a calibrated horizontal scale. The pointer remains at the point of farthest travel and thereby allows an easy determination of the total horizontal distance, $D$. Thus, minute differences in the value of $h$ can be easily determined from the value of $D$, which is seen as much larger differences along the scale.‡ In practice, the horizontal

‡ If the length of the pendulum arm is $L$ and the horizontal distance traveled by the pointer is $D$, it can be shown that $h = L - \sqrt{L^2 - D^2}$

scale can be laid out directly in velocity units, depending on the weight of the bullet, the weight of the mass, and the length of the arm. To help illustrate this, we can set up the following example. If, as in the keg example, we let the projectile weigh one pound and the large mass 250 pounds, then we again have the relationship:

$$V = 2000\sqrt{h}$$

If the length of the pendulum arm is chosen at 10 feet, then the values of the vertical height $h$ and the horizontal distance $D$ can be summarized in the following table for a few assumed values of the projectile velocity.

TABLE 9

| Velocity (ft per sec) | Vertical Height h (inches) | Horizontal Travel D (inches) |
|---|---|---|
| 900 | 2.4 | 24.0 |
| 950 | 2.7 | 25.4 |
| 1000 | 3.0 | 26.7 |
| 1050 | 3.3 | 28.0 |
| 1100 | 3.6 | 29.3 |

Robins first used his ballistic pendulum to measure the velocities of musket balls, which he was able to do with an accuracy of between two and five parts in one thousand. Although eventually superseded by the ballistic chronograph, the ballistic pendulum is still used for various purposes, such as the measure of a gun's total recoil momentum. Its utter simplicity in construction, moreover, still makes it very popular with the amateur experimenter.

## 2. The Ballistic Chronograph

A chronograph is any instrument that measures and records time. The stopwatch is perhaps the most commonly

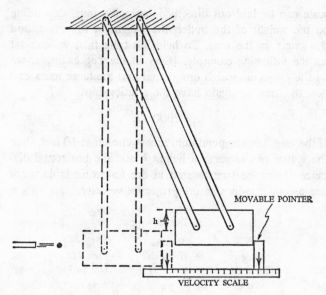

Fig. 15. Ballistic pendulum.

known device fitting this definition. Generally, the time
interval measured by a chronograph can be translated directly into a velocity. For example, if a sprinter's time
for the 100-yard dash is clocked at 10 seconds, simple
arithmetic shows that he traveled the 300 feet at an average velocity of 30 feet per second. Similarly, the average
velocity of any moving body can be determined by observing the time interval it takes to traverse a measured
distance between two reference marks. For objects traveling much faster than sprinters, the time intervals are correspondingly smaller, and the precise instant that a reference marker is passed becomes more difficult to determine.
A very fast train can travel 300 feet in two seconds, while
a rifle bullet can do it in less than one-tenth second. An
alert man with an excellent stopwatch might make a fair
guess of the train's speed, but he and his stopwatch are

powerless when it comes to estimating bullet velocities. For this purpose, he needs a much superior chronograph, one which must possess two essential features: it must have a timing mechanism that can measure extremely small time intervals with a high degree of precision, and it must incorporate a reliable means for starting the timer at the precise instant the projectile passes the first reference point and for stopping it when the projectile passes the second reference point. A ballistic chronograph is a device that has these two features. As the name implies, it is an instrument that specifically measures and records the time it takes a projectile to travel between two reference points.

The first successful ballistic chronograph was developed in 1874 by Captain Paul Emil le Boulengé of the Belgian Army. His system uses a timer connected to two screens, each of which consists of a frame on which a fine wire is strung. The wire in the first screen forms part of an electric circuit which activates an electromagnet that supports a tubular piece of metal. When the projectile pierces the first screen, the wire is snapped, the electric circuit is broken, and the electromagnet immediately loses its magnetism. As a result, the metal tube falls. While this tube is in free fall, the projectile is traveling toward the second screen, which also has wire network that is part of an electric circuit activating an electromagnet. When the wire is broken, the deactivated electromagnet releases a steel weight that falls against a trigger, which in turn activates a spring-loaded knife that darts out and makes a mark on the metal tube which is still falling. The time for the projectile to travel between the first and second screens can then be determined directly by the relative location of this mark on the tube. The Boulengé chronograph, as it is more commonly known, was more accurate than the ballistic pendulum, since it could measure a velocity level to within one part in one thousand. It was also more convenient to use than the ballistic pendulum, which required the periodic replacement of the large mass which became badly mutilated after a number of firings. The Boulengé chronograph remained the standard system for measuring muzzle velocities for over a half century, and was still in very common use after World War II.

A substantial improvement over the Boulengé chronograph was made with the development of an electronic timer that could measure time intervals with much more accuracy than a falling weight. The heart of this counter is a high-frequency oscillating circuit, originally developed for counting the radioactive rays from a Geiger counter. The electronic counter consists of three basic elements: an oscillator, with a typical frequency of 100,000 oscillations per second; a gate circuit, which is opened by one electrical signal from an outside source and which is then closed by a second electrical signal; and a counting circuit, which counts and then registers the number of pulses or oscillations which went through the gate during the interval it was open. The gate circuit is connected to the two screens. When the projectile goes through the first screen the counting circuit is activated; when it goes through the second screen the counting circuit is shut off. The total time elapsed is then shown directly on the face of the instrument. This ballistic chronograph is a sort of electronic stopwatch that is started and stopped by electrical impulses and which can measure a time interval to within one hundred thousandth of a second.

The accuracy of a ballistic chronograph depends also on the accuracy with which the electric signals from the screens start and stop the timer. The screen already described with the Boulengé chronograph consists of a fine wire network, which when ruptured causes an electric current passing through the wire to be interrupted. This type of screen has some objectionable features, since a variable amount of electrical contact may be made through the projectile itself. The exact instant at which the current is broken does not always correspond to a constant position to the projectile, and thus some error is possible. Moreover, as the projectile passes the first screen, the mass of the wire itself may influence the velocity of the projectile. For these reasons, other types of screens have been tried and used, many of which give improved performance characteristics. There are various types of screens commonly used for velocity measurement, so a brief description of their performance may be of interest.

The Aberdeen or "sandwich" screen was developed at the U. S. Army Ordnance Aberdeen Proving Ground, and consists of two conducting foils separated by an insulating film. When the projectile nose penetrates the sandwich, it acts as a conductor and permits current to flow from one foil to the next. The sudden flow of current is then used to actuate a timer. Although an improvement over the break-wire type of screen, the projectile must still displant a small mass as it moves through the screen. This difficulty is completely obviated by the solenoid screen, which has the advantage of not requiring projectile contact with any part of the screen. When the magnetized projectile passes through a large circular coil of wire, a change in voltage is generated by magnetic induction and a current is thereby induced in the coil. This change in current is amplified and made to act as a signal for actuating or stopping a timer. However, the most successful type of screen in use today is the photoelectric screen, which consists of a frame with a light source and a photoelectric cell. The source directs a sheet, or beam, of light against a slit, behind which is the photoelectric cell. As the projectile passes through, it interrupts the beam and thereby causes a slight change in the intensity of light being picked up by the photoelectric cell. The cell converts the change in light intensity into a change in current, and this in turn generates a signal to the timer. In modern practice, the photoelectric screen, combined with the electronic counter, provides an extremely reliable ballistic chronograph that is easily capable of measuring a projectile's velocity to within one part in five thousand.

## THE MEASUREMENT OF PRESSURE

Benjamin Robins can, in one way, be credited with being the first individual to measure the average pressure inside a gun. He was a first-rate mathematician, who was thoroughly familiar with Newton's work, and he could use the velocity measurements obtained with his ballistic pendulum, calculate the projectile energy, and from this he could easily calculate the average pressure in the gun tube.¶ However, it was not the average pressure that burst gun barrels, and the need remained for the measurement of the peak, or maximum pressure. Robins also tried to calculate peak pressures by assuming that all the propellant was burned before the projectile began to move and by using an incorrect thermodynamic relationship between instantaneous pressure and total volume behind the projectile during its movement down the bore. The error in his method was due to the lack of thermodynamic data at the time, but his estimates of peak pressure were nevertheless approximate. In any event, peak pressures were not to be known until they could be measured.

There are basically two kinds of pressure measure-

---

¶ Since *energy*, $E$ = *average force* times the *distance*, $D$ over which the force acts (distance traveled in the barrel), and since *average force* = *average pressure*, $\bar{P}$ times *area*, $A$, against which the pressure acts (equal to bore cross-sectional area), then $E = \bar{P}AD$. But the bore area $A$ times the length $D$ is also equal to the volume $V$ through which the projectile traveled. Hence, $E = \bar{P}V$ or $\bar{P} = E/V$. All terms must be expressed in consistent units. If $E$ is given in foot-pounds, and $V$ in cubic feet, then $\bar{P}$ will be in pounds per square foot.

ments: one merely measures the peak pressure reached in the barrel, while the other more sophisticated method continuously measures pressure throughout the complete time cycle. Peak pressure measurements are the more commonly useful. For example, when lots of ammunition are manufactured, samples of the ammunition are used to obtain peak pressure and measurements and the lot of ammunition is not released unless the peak pressures fall below rigidly held specifications. Since every gun manufactured by a reliable concern has been fired at least once £ with a round of ammunition that greatly exceeds the peak pressure specification, the sportsman is assured that no round of ammunition he buys will ever exceed a pressure which the gun has endured. The measurement of pressure-time for the complete cycle during which the projectile travels in the bore is, as discussed in Chapter 5, useful in studying the behavior of the entire interior ballistic cycle.

## 1. The Measurement of Peak Pressure

In 1869, Sir Andrew Noble obtained the first reliable determination of the maximum pressure in a gun barrel with an apparatus such as the one represented in Figure 16. With but minor modifications, this same type of pressure gauge is still in common use today. Its operation is simple and straightforward. As the pressure in the chamber rises, it exerts a force against the steel piston, which in turn deforms a copper cylinder located against an anvil. The degree to which the copper cylinder is deformed is then directly related to the peak pressure.

Copper cylinders are made to accurate standard dimen-

£ This is known as proof firing (i.e., proving the barrel's strength), and is done with special ammunition that exceeds the peak pressure specification. After the gun has been fired, a proof mark is stamped on the barrel.

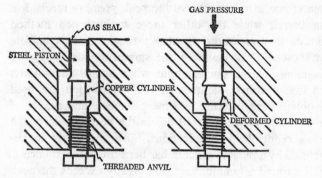

Fig. 16. Interior of pressure gauge chamber.

sions, and still record given pressure levels with a very high consistency. They are generally used for peak pressures of 15,000 psi and above, while lead cylinders are used in crusher gauges for peak pressures below this level, such as with shot shell ammunition. This measurement of peak pressure, together with a measure of muzzle velocity, represent the two most important and commonly used measurements in use even today. As previously mentioned, every lot of ammunition has peak pressure and muzzle velocity specifications, and measurements of both quantities are taken from a sample of each lot to ensure that both measurements fall within the prescribed limits.

## 2. The Measurement of Pressure-Time

The first highly accurate, simply obtainable pressure-time records were made by taking advantage of the piezo-electric effect. There are certain materials, such as quartz and tourmeline, which exhibit a unique but very useful phenomenon: when compressed, they generate a small charge of electricity; this charge, moreover, is directly proportional to the pressure acting to compress it. In 1917, Sir J. J. Thomson, the British physicist, applied this phenomenon to the measurement of pressures in gun barrels by the use of a quartz crystal mounted in the barrel. As the pressure builds up in the barrel, a steel cylinder is forced against the quartz crystal and causes it to be compressed. This crystal then translates the continuous change in pressure applied to it into an exactly corresponding electrical charge. This electrical charge, however, is extremely small and, even at the high pressures encountered in gun barrels, does not exceed one-ten-millionth of a coulomb.§ This faint electrical charge is amplified and then fed onto the plate in a cathode ray tube. This is a tube which works like the picture tube in a television set. It contains a gas at low pressure and is characterized by the emission of a stream of negatively charged particles, known as cathode rays. When these fall upon the phosphorescent face of the tube, a brilliant illumination is produced. The beam, however, travels between two horizontal plates. If a plate is positively charged, the beam is attracted toward it. Now if the charge from the quartz crystal is put on the upper plate, it will cause the beam to be deflected upward by an amount directly proportional to the pressure. In the meantime, the beam is made to move across the screen horizontally to represent time. As the beam moves horizontally, it is also deflected upward by a varying amount and the result is a plot, which when converted to proper units, shows pressure versus time. A camera placed over the screen is usually used to record a pressure-time trace, like the one shown in Chapter 5.

## MEASUREMENT OF THE PROPELLANT CHARACTERISTICS

From the earliest days of black powder, its manufacturers were in continuous search for more powerful for-

§ One coulomb is the quantity of electricity transferred by one ampere in one second.

mulations. This prompted a few of the more careful experimenters to devise methods for measuring the relative strengths of different powders. Devices for doing this date from the sixteenth century and consisted generally of an apparatus with a small chamber, a touchhole, and a heavy lid. Explosion of the propellant drove the lid upward (like the keg in Figure 13), and the height to which it rose was used as a measure of propellant power. Such contraptions were generally unsatisfactory and gave but rough unreliable quantitative comparisons between propellants. Suitable means for measuring propellant characteristics were not possible until after Noble had developed the measurement of peak pressures. The measurement of propellant-burning characteristics are made in a device known as a ballistic bomb.*

A ballistic bomb is simply a thick-walled steel vessel with an interval chamber having a volume of generally 5 to 15 cubic inches. A pressure gauge and a means for electrical or mechanical ignition of the propellant are incorporated into the bomb. In a test of a given propellant, it will be loaded with various quantities of propellant, typically filling from 5 per cent to 20 per cent of the volume. By relating the measured peak pressure to the chamber volume and quantity of propellant, it is possible to obtain values of the propellant energy content and its co-volume. Also from measurement of the rate of pressure rise, the ballistician can calculate the propellant's burn rate characteristics.

Bomb measurements are not in the strictest sense interior ballistic measurements (since they are not made on a gun). Nevertheless, they are extremely useful in assessing the performance of a propellant. As was made evident in Chapter 3, a propellant used for a specific ammunition

---

* In Britain it is called a closed vessel.

must have a geometry and a burning behavior that is controlled within narrow limits. Bomb tests are used to help ensure that a lot of propellant meets its performance specifications.

# CHAPTER 7

# THE INTERIOR BALLISTICS
# OF ROCKETS

For centuries the moon has been associated with romance, lunacy, or the ebb and flow of the tides. When Galileo built his telescope and discovered the strange mountainous crater-filled character of the lunar surface, he aroused a curiosity as to what kinds of beings might populate this eerie world. As larger telescopes were built and the lunar terrain became better known, this curiosity inevitably grew into a preoccupation with actually going to the moon. Although this was seemingly impossible, the wish to go there fathered a large number of fanciful stories in which the voyage was made by means of a giant balloon, or by a tremendous wind that blew a ship up off the water and carried it all the way to the lunar surface, or even by the use of strange substances that were repelled by the earth's gravitational force. The most plausible and imaginative of all these tales was Jules Verne's *Voyage to the Moon,* which appeared in 1865 and became, until recent times, the classic moon-trip story.

Verne's spaceship was a cabin nine feet in diameter "fired" from a nine-hundred-foot-long cannon. The cabin had one-foot-thick aluminum walls and a padded interior for three passengers. Motive power was provided by two hundred tons of nitrocellulose (which had been discovered by Schönbein less than twenty years before and was not yet at that time developed in a form suitable for a propellant). Jules Verne was not only a masterful science-fiction storyteller; he also took great pains to make his tales technically plausible. He knew that a projectile must have a velocity of about 36,000 ft/sec in order to escape the earth's gravitation. He also knew that air resistance would slow down a projectile before it could pass through the atmosphere (although he did not know how much), and so he determined that the cabin must be accelerated to a velocity of 54,000 ft/sec in the cannon. For his time, Verne's moon-gun was imaginative, daring, and well thought out. However, in the light of what we know today it is easy to show that his moon-gun would be absolutely unworkable for a great number of reasons. For one, on the basis of considerations covered in Chapter 5 we know such a gun cannot really attain even one-tenth the 54,000 ft/sec velocity. The necessary acceleration in the gun, moreover, would kill the passengers instantly. Even if a projectile reached the atmosphere at this velocity it would be instantly vaporized by the tremendous heat of air friction. An analysis of Verne's moon-gun can be used to conclude that a gun is not a suitable mechanism for sending a projectile to the moon. The only way to get there is with an ancient device that was thought to have been made obsolete centuries ago by the invention of the gun. This device is a rocket.

The process that makes a rocket work is an interior ballistic process very similar to the one that takes place inside a gun. A propellant converts its chemical energy into heat which is stored in the gases released by the reaction. The hot gases cause high pressures in the chamber, and these in turn force a gaseous stream to flow out of an orifice at a very high velocity. As these gases are accelerated, or "fired" out of the nozzle the rocket recoils. It is this recoil that moves the rocket.

The purpose of this chapter is to present a brief historical background on the development of rockets, to explain how a rocket works, to discuss the types of rocket propellants, and finally to describe the interior ballistic phenomena that occur inside a rocket motor and to show how they are similar to those that occur in a gun.

## HISTORICAL BACKGROUND

The early history of rockets is intimately related to that of black powder simply because rockets used black powder for propulsion. It seems probable that rockets in some primitive form antedated the gun by a few centuries. The history of the rocket, however, is every bit as vague as the history of black powder. Many of the references on the subject confidently impute its invention to the Chinese, although the available historical sources do little more than mention their use of "arrows of flying fire" against the Mongols and other unfriendly neighbors. These old sources also suggest that the Arabs were next to learn the secret of the rocket and from them it came to Europe. By the year 1400 the use of rockets, principally for military purposes, was fairly well known. They very much resembled the black powder rockets that are still in use today for fireworks displays, and consisted of three basic parts: a tube into which was tapped black powder with a provision for its burning in a particular way; a guiding stick, which acted to stabilize it in flight so that the rocket would always fly nose on; and the payload, which was the remaining mass of the rocket at the time it reached its target and which was sometimes augmented by a separate charge of black powder in the nose, hopefully intended to ignite on impact. For the most part the old rockets were unreliable, grossly inaccurate, and capable of little damage. As early as 1400 the crude guns of the time were definitely superior weapons, and as a result the rocket was virtually made obsolete. Apparently its only military value was the confidence it gave the user that he was frightening the enemy. In spite of these deficiencies the rocket had one very attractive feature. It required only a thin tube, or a grooved board, for a launcher. This was particularly important to the military engineers faced with the prodigious problems of moving enormous cannons over nonexistent roads with nothing but muscle-power. For this reason there were periodic attempts to develop a better rocket. During the four centuries from 1400 to 1800, enthusiasm for rockets went up and down like a Yo-Yo. Yet in spite of the best efforts of military engineers, rockets could not be made either lethal or accurate. As a result the rocket finally came to be cursed and thoroughly discounted as a meaningful weapon.

This state of affairs was suddenly changed in the 1790s by a series of military disasters that befell the British in India. They suffered a number of disconcerting defeats caused largely by the Indians' surprising use of large rockets, which they rained down on the British in profuse quantities. These rockets employed iron tubes for the powder charge, which made larger propellant charges possible and thus permitted a much heavier payload. The heavier powder charges and larger masses gave them a terminal energy sufficiently high to overcome the problem of lethality. Moreover, by the clever use of great multiplicities of rockets in salvos, the problem of accuracy was overcome by the sheer weight of numbers. The British were very quick to react to these defeats and did so with an intense revival of interest in rockets, personified by the activities of inventor William Congreve. He gathered all the available know-how, and by applying a sound engineering approach succeeded in developing a very much improved 32-lb incendiary rocket that had a range of about two miles and a black powder warhead. In spite of their much greater lethality the accuracy of his rockets was still not particularly good. About the best he could do was to set one off on one side of a river and generally hit a town on the other. However, his new rockets could deliver a lot of damage, and what they lacked in accuracy could be made up by gross numbers. In 1807, for example, one barrage of 25,000 Congreve rockets succeeded in destroying more than half the city of Copenhagen. A rocket bombardment of Baltimore during the War of 1812 inspired a Maryland lawyer to write "The Star-Spangled Banner," in which reference is made to "the rocket's red glare." In spite of a few successes in bombarding cities, the advantages of Congreve's rockets were short-lived. The accuracy, the range, and the lethality of artillery shells were greatly improved, and these could outperform the rockets of the time. Accordingly, the rocket again appeared headed for oblivion.

A revival of interest occurred early in the present century with the publication of three articles, each of which almost went unnoticed, by three men working independently in Russia, the United States, and Germany. The first, published in 1903, was written by Constantin Ziolkovsky, who wrote on the requirements for a spaceship in which he identified a rocket as the necessary means for propulsion and a high-energy fuel as necessary to obtain the necessary velocity levels. The second paper, titled "A Method for Reaching Extreme Altitudes" and published in 1919, was written by Dr. Robert Goddard, an American physics professor; this paper also discussed the use of high-energy liquid propellants to power a rocket into space. The third paper, published in 1923, was written by Hermann Oberth, whose thesis was that "the present state of science and of technological knowledge permits the building of machines that can rise beyond the limits of the atmosphere." It is interesting to note that all three were concerned with the problem of sending a vehicle into space, and each identified two requirements: a rocket to propel the vehicle, and a high-energy propellant to give it the requisite velocity. The efforts of these three scientists precipitated the efforts of their three countries into the pursuit of rocket technology. At first this effort went on quietly and the results were regarded principally as a scientific curiosity. However, when World War II broke out, intensive efforts were made to realize any military potential in rockets. This culminated in the development of the dread German V-2, which could deliver hundreds of pounds of explosive a hundred miles away with deadly accuracy. As everyone knows today, the developments in rocketry since World War II have been nothing short of phenomenal. Rockets can now be made to put tons of payload into precise orbits and to touch down on other worlds.

## WHAT MAKES A ROCKET WORK

A rubber balloon that is blown up and then released will whizz away and fly around until its air is exhausted. The reason for the balloon's motion and the basic principle of rocket propulsion are the same. This can be illustrated with the help of Figure 17. If a gas is compressed in a closed container it will exert a pressure equal and opposite in all directions. Accordingly the force in any one direction is counterbalanced by a force in the opposite direction, and as a result the net forces acting on the container are all neutralized. As is shown in Figure 17(a) each of the arrows, representing the pressure acting to push the container in any given direction, is exactly counterbalanced by one pushing in the opposite direction. Suppose that a hole is suddenly punched at one end of the container. The pressure at the hole will drop to normal atmospheric pressure, but the pressure acting against the opposite wall will not be counterbalanced and so the container will be accelerated, as is shown in Figure 17(b). Of course, once the opening is made the pressurized air inside the container will quickly rush out the aperture and the pressure on the inside will fall to the atmospheric pressure level on the outside; as a result no further motion will take place. In a rocket this pressure is continuously built up within the container by means of a propellant which is converted into a gas at a known and controlled rate.

*(a)*

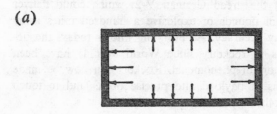

*(b)*

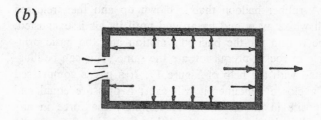

*(c)*

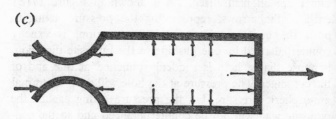

Fig. 17. A schematic representation of the basic principles of rocket propulsion: (*a*) Pressure of gases in receptacle is equalized in all directions. (*b*) Pressure of gases is unbalanced so receptacle is accelerated to the right. (*c*) Use of nozzle greatly increases the pressure unbalance.

A hole punched in at one end of a container would work somewhat inefficiently. The effectiveness of a rocket is very greatly increased by using a nozzle-shaped orifice, as shown in Figure 17(c). The contoured walls near the orifice reduce the friction of gas flow, and the act of going out through the constriction causes the gas to be further accelerated because it expands. This in turn results in additional pressures on the wall of the nozzle that increase the net total pressure acting to accelerate the rocket. In practice the rate at which propellant is burned is controlled so that a certain pressure builds up inside the rocket. The action of the throat in the nozzle then limits the flow of gas in such a way that the pressure inside the rocket motor remains constant.

This explanation of a rocket's motion is analogous to that of a gun's recoil motion. It is caused by the pressure which acts not only to accelerate the projectile out the muzzle but which also acts to accelerate the gun rearward. However, in discussing a gun's motion it is easier to calculate its recoil velocity if we know the gun's and projectile's weights and the projectile velocity. Similarly, it is more direct to calculate the rocket's motion from known values of propellant and rocket weight and of the velocity of the gas stream rushing out the nozzle.

### NEWTON'S LAW AND THE MASS RATIO

The motion of a rocket is also simply explainable by Newton's Third Law of Motion, "To every action there is always an equal and opposite reaction." As shown in Chapter 4, the physical consequences of this law can be expressed by the equivalence of momentum, which is given by the relationship:

$$MV = mv$$

where $M$ and $m$ are the masses of two bodies and $V$ and $v$ are their velocities respectively. This relationship was used in Chapter 4 to obtain the velocity of a recoiling gun. Rocket motion is identically analogous to gun recoil motion. A rocket moves simply because it is "recoiling" from the act of firing a multiplicity of gaseous bullets. It would therefore seem that if $M$ is the mass of the rocket, $m$ the mass of the propellant in the rocket, and $v$ the velocity of the gases flowing out the nozzle, then the final velocity $V$ achieved by the rocket should be directly obtainable from our equivalence of momentum equation and we would have

$$V = (m/M)v$$

or

(rocket velocity) = (ratio of masses) times (gas velocity)

This is not quite true. The rocket velocity, $V$, will be less than is predicted by the above equation and the reason for this can be explained in part as follows: Suppose we have a 4-lb gun that fires a 4-lb projectile at a velocity of 1000 ft/sec (we will discount here the mass of the propellant that moves it). From our momentum formula, it is quickly evident that the gun will be given a recoil velocity of 1000 ft/sec. At this point we might conclude that if a 4-lb rocket contained 4 lbs of rocket propellant (for a total of 8 lbs) and if the propellant was all converted into gases that shot out of the nozzle at 1000 ft/sec, then the rocket should also achieve a velocity of 1000 ft/sec. The propellant, however, does not all flow out in one "shot," but instead flows continuously. In so doing, the portion of propellant that flows out is actually causing the 4 lbs of rocket plus the remaining fuel to recoil. This point can be more easily seen if we assume that a 2-lb gun fires two projectiles that weigh 1 lb each.

As the first projectile is fired, the 2-lb gun and the second 1-lb projectile (which is still in the gun) will *both* be given a recoil velocity, and so a 3-lb mass will recoil when a 1-lb projectile is fired. Our momentum equation then says that

$$3 \cdot V_1 = 1 \cdot (1000)$$

from which we see that the gun's recoil velocity $V_1$ given by the first shot is 333 ft/sec. Now when the second 2-lb shot is fired, it causes the 2-lb gun to be given a further increment in velocity, as determined by the relationship

$$2 \cdot V_2 = 1 \cdot (1000)$$
or
$$V_2 = 500 \text{ ft/sec}$$

Thus the gun is given a total recoil velocity, in two stages, of 333 + 500 = 833 ft/sec, which is somewhat less than the 1000 ft/sec obtained if all 2 lbs of projectile were fired at once. If we now go on to consider a 2-lb gun firing four $\frac{1}{2}$-lb projectiles in succession, we can calculate the four individual increments of velocity as follows:

*First Shot:* A $3\frac{1}{2}$-lb mass, consisting of a 2-lb gun plus three $\frac{1}{2}$-lb projectiles, is made to recoil by a $\frac{1}{2}$-lb projectile fired with 1000 ft/sec velocity.

Hence
$$(3 \cdot 5) V_1 = (\tfrac{1}{2})(1000)$$
so
$$V_1 = 143$$

*Second Shot:* A 3-lb mass, consisting of a 2-lb gun plus two $\frac{1}{2}$-lb projectiles, is made to recoil by the second $\frac{1}{2}$-lb projectile fired with 1000 ft/sec velocity.

Hence
$$3V_2 = (\tfrac{1}{2})(1000)$$
so
$$V_2 = 167$$

*Third Shot:* A $2\frac{1}{2}$-lb mass, consisting of a 2-lb gun plus one $\frac{1}{2}$-lb projectile, is made to recoil by the third $\frac{1}{2}$-lb projectile fired with 1000 ft/sec velocity.

Hence $\qquad (2 \cdot 5)V_3 = (\frac{1}{2})(1000)$
so $\qquad\qquad\quad V_3 = 200$

*Fourth Shot:* The 2-lb gun is made to recoil by the remaining $\frac{1}{2}$-lb projectile fired at 1000 ft/sec velocity.

Hence $\qquad\quad 2V_4 = (\frac{1}{2})(1000)$
so $\qquad\qquad\quad V_4 = 250$

The total velocity imparted to the rocket is equal to $V_1 + V_2 + V_3 + V_4$ or 760 ft/sec. If we were to continue this process of dividing the 2 lbs of projectile into a larger number of smaller projectiles we would arrive at an even lower velocity, which would turn out to be 693 ft/sec. Thus where the simple recoil formula predicts 1000 ft/sec, we actually get only 693 ft/sec. The reason for this, again, is that the unburned portion of the propellant adds mass to the portion that is being accelerated by the burned gases flowing out the nozzle. A derivation of the formula that predicts the rocket's final velocity is beyond the scope of this book but that need not stop us from using it. It can be written

$$\text{rocket velocity} = V = v_e ln(1 + m/M)$$

where $v_e$ is the gas velocity
$\qquad m$ is the propellant mass
$\qquad M$ is the mass of the rocket
$\qquad\qquad$ (exclusive of propellant)

The expression $ln(1 + m/M)$ represents the natural logarithm of $(1 + m/M)$. The extent to which the value of $ln(1 + m/M)$ departs from $m/M$ is seen from Table 10, which lists a few example values.

TABLE 10

| $m/M$ | $ln(1+m/M)$ |
|---|---|
| .01 | .010 |
| .03 | .030 |
| .05 | .049 |
| .07 | .068 |
| .10 | .095 |
| .30 | .262 |
| .50 | .405 |
| .70 | .531 |
| 1.00 | .693 |
| 3.00 | 1.386 |
| 5.00 | 1.792 |
| 7.00 | 2.079 |
| 10.00 | 2.398 |

We can see that if the value of $m/M$ is very small, that is, if the ratio of rocket weight to propellant weight is very low, then there is little difference between $m/M$ and $ln(1 + m/M)$. However, as $m/M$ becomes large, the difference also becomes large. These numbers will take on a little more meaning if we convert them into rocket velocities. We will first assume three kinds of propellants: the first burns in such a way that the gas velocity $v_e$ out the nozzle is 2000 ft/sec; for the second, $v_e = 6000$ ft/sec; and for the third, $v_e = 10,000$ ft/sec. We can now use the all-important equation

$$\text{final rocket velocity} = V = v_e ln(1 + m/M)$$

This very quickly shows the importance of the two quantities $(m/M)$ and $v_e$. The quantity $m/M$ is used in the all-important characteristics of a rocket known as the mass ratio. This is the ratio of the rocket's total mass before launching to its remaining mass after all the fuel is burned up. The total mass is the weight of propellant

TABLE 11
ROCKET VELOCITIES
[$m$ = propellant wt; $M$ = payload wt]

| $m/M$ | $ln(1+m/M)$ | $v_e ln(1+m/M)$ | | |
|---|---|---|---|---|
| | | $v_e = 2000$ | $v_e = 6000$ | $v_e = 10,000$ |
| .01 | .010 | 20 | 60 | 100 |
| .03 | .030 | 60 | 180 | 300 |
| .05 | .049 | 98 | 294 | 490 |
| .07 | .068 | 136 | 408 | 680 |
| .10 | .095 | 190 | 570 | 950 |
| .30 | .262 | 512 | 1536 | 2620 |
| .50 | .405 | 810 | 2430 | 4050 |
| .70 | .531 | 1062 | 3186 | 5310 |
| 1.00 | .693 | 1386 | 4158 | 6930 |
| 3.00 | 1.386 | 2772 | 8316 | 13,860 |
| 5.00 | 1.792 | 3584 | 10,750 | 17,920 |

*and* payload, or $= m + M$. The mass ratio, $R$, is thus equal to $(m + M)/M$, which we can see is also equal to $1 + m/M$

Hence $R = 1 + m/M$

In the future we can therefore write the equation for a rocket's terminal velocity in the form

$$V = v_e ln R$$

Going back up to the table we note that for the values of $m/M$ and of $v_e$ that we chose there is no combination that will give us a value that comes even close to the 36,-000 escape velocity. It so happens that a ratio of $m/M =$ 10.00 and a $v_e$ greater than 10,000 ft/sec are possible with today's structural engineering and propellant technology. The trick to getting higher velocity is by the use of more than one stage. Suppose we have a rocket that is 80 per cent for propellant, 15 per cent for rocket structure, and 5 per cent for an additional structure. Thus

$m = 80$ and $M = 20$ for $m/M = 4.00$. If the propellant has a nozzle velocity $v_e = 10,000$ ft/sec, then the table alone shows that the terminal velocity of the 15 per cent and 5 per cent structures is 13,860 ft/sec. Now if the 5 per cent structure is also a rocket where 4 per cent is propellant and 1 per cent structure, and this rocket separates from the first one when its fuel is used up, it can achieve an additional increment of 13,860 ft/sec. Thus 1 per cent of the original mass can be accelerated to 27,-720 ft/sec.

These figures should not be taken for anything more than examples to show how the use of more than one "stage" can provide almost any velocity needed, although it becomes quickly apparent that the final payload is necessarily a fraction of the total mass.

The achievement of high mass ratios is an engineering accomplishment made possible by today's advanced technology in structures. The other element in the equation $V = v_e ln R$ is the velocity characteristics of the propellant, which will be covered next.

## ROCKET PROPELLANTS

As in a gun, the rocket propellant is a substance in which chemical energy is stored. Also, as in a gun, this chemical energy is released as the propellant decomposes into a gaseous form. The chemical energy is stored in these gases in the form of heat and is subsequently converted to the energy of high-velocity flow out the nozzle. Thus, as the molecules of gas are formed the heat energy that is simultaneously released agitates these molecules into their characteristic high-velocity random motion (discussed in Chapter 3), and this in turn results in a high-velocity gas stream out the nozzle. There are two principal types of rocket propellants: solid and liquid.

Solid propellants used in rockets are of two types: the

double-base propellants and the composite propellants. The double-base propellants are nitrocellulose-nitroglycerin and are very much like the propellants used in guns; the principal difference is in their physical shape. Composite propellants are, as the name implies, a physical mixture of a fuel and an oxidizer, sometimes with an additional substance to help bind them together. Black powder is in a real sense a composite propellant, as it requires carbon as a fuel, potassium nitrate as an oxidizer, and a third material, sulfur, to help bind the material together. Potassium nitrate is still one of the common oxidizers used today. The fuels commonly used in solid propellants are either asphalt oil type, or plastic or rubber type. Asphalt, for example, is a bituminous hydrocarbon that can be heated and liquefied to mix with the oxidizer and thereby form solid grains with suitable physical properties. The plastic materials are also used for fuels since they combine readily with oxygen and can also be mixed with the oxidizer and cast into suitable grains by virtue of the very plastic property of the fuel itself. Rubber type fuels are also usable since some of the synthetic rubbers will oxidize well and their elastic properties make them suitable for the fabrication of solid grains. Solid propellants usually exist as single large grains cast into blocks of prechosen geometry. During combustion, the whole area where the propellant is stored is under pressure, and so the carefully controlled burning rate depends on this pressure, the shape of the grain, and the initial temperature. Whereas shotguns have peak pressures of approximately 10,000 psi and high-powered rifles tolerate peak pressures of 50,000 psi, a rocket motor, by virtue of its necessity for lightness, will generally operate at 1000 psi or less. This pressure, incidentally, is carefully controlled by the area of the burning surface, by the volume available to the gases, and by the properties of the nozzle. By a proper balance between these three prechosen properties, fairly constant pressure level can be maintained.

One very important reason for good physical properties is the need for these grains to maintain their structural integrity during burning. If the grain cracks, the flame will shoot along the crack and this will greatly increase the burning surface and in turn increase the rate of gas generation. This will immediately start a chain reaction: first the added surface available to burning will cause the rate of gas generation to go up; however, the nozzle will then be unable to discharge the gases as fast as they are generated. As a result the pressure level will go up. This increase in pressure level will also cause the burning rate to increase, and so a pressure level will quickly be reached which will burst the chamber. Rockets exploding in this manner have been a common experience with countless experimenters. Where no provision was made for physical protection, many of these explosions had disastrous effects.

The one real advantage of solid propellants is their simplicity. Most solid propellants can be stored easily over long periods of time and are thus ready for immediate use. When a solid propellant is used, the storage chamber is a part of the combustion chamber, and no pumping or control system is needed, but the propellant grain itself must be sturdy enough to withstand the high operating pressures in the combustion chamber. It is for this reason that solid propellants have been largely limited to employment in rockets with relatively short ranges. Most of the modern solid propellant units employ a technique of manufacture in which the propellant is cast within the case, and through use of a bonding agent is firmly cemented to the metal or plastic wall. The propellant grain, as the solid block is called, is sometimes cast with a hole down the center. This hole, called the perforation, may have a variety of shapes. The choice of perforation shape and dimension is one way of establishing the burning rate, that is, the rate of the reaction.

Liquid propellants offer two principal advantages: first they give better control since the rate of burning is determined not by the area of a burning surface, but rather by regulation of the rate at which liquids are introduced into the combustion chamber. The second advantage is that much more energy can be obtained from suitable combinations of liquid fuels and liquid oxidizers. A prime example is the use of liquid hydrogen as a fuel and liquid oxygen as the oxidizer, which can give a specific impulse of approximately 400. Liquid-fuel systems are either monofuel or bifuel. In monofuel systems a single liquid supplies both the fuel and oxidizing material. In the bifuel systems two liquids are used. One is the fuel, the other the oxidizer. Naturally, the bifuel systems are complicated, but generally they have the advantage that neither liquid by itself is explosive.

When liquid propellants are used, they are not ordinarily stored in the combustion chamber but are forced into it at a controlled rate. If the liquid is stored under pressure, the tanks must be of heavy construction, and the rocket has the same weight handicap as one burning a solid propellant. If the liquid is stored at low pressure, the storage tanks can be lightweight and the ratio of initial weight to final weight is more favorable, provided the rocket is large. In today's large rockets, mass ratios as high as 10 to 1 are possible.

For very high terminal velocities it is necessary for the combustion process to last for a long period of time. The metals within the combustion chamber and nozzle would soon deteriorate if directly exposed to the great heat developed here. The commonly used method of cooling is to route the initially cold liquid propellant fuel through ducts or passages in contact with the hot chamber walls. This, in turn, warms the fuel on its way to combustion.

The technique, called "regenerative" cooling, is beneficial to the efficiency of the entire combustion process.

## INTERIOR BALLISTIC PROCESSES IN A ROCKET

A rocket, like a gun, is a heat engine that converts the chemical energy stored in a propellant into the kinetic energy of a body that is thereby given a high velocity. A rocket differs from a gun in two principal respects. First, in a gun the propellant gases act to accelerate a projectile, while in a rocket they accelerate themselves into a high-velocity gas stream out the muzzle. Thus, when our genie of the propellant is in a gun he uses his powers to hurl a projectile out the muzzle. When he is in a rocket he throws himself out. The second difference lies in the reaction time. In a gun the total process occurs in one relatively brief pulse that ends as the projectile leaves the muzzle. In a rocket the reaction takes place continuously for a much greater period of time. In order to maintain this continuous combustion process the rocket must have the capability of storing a great quantity of propellant. Some rocket structures can hold ten times their own weight in fuel, while guns virtually always weigh hundreds of times as much as their propellant charge. Nevertheless, in spite of these differences between guns and rockets, the interior ballistic characteristics of each are very similar. The similarities in the chemical, the thermodynamic, and the physical processes that occur in both guns and rockets can be made more easily evident by direct comparison.

The nature of the chemical phenomena that take place inside a rocket is basically the same as those in a gun. All of the rocket propellants discussed above, for example, share with nitrocellulose two important characteristics of the decomposition process: the sudden and complete conversion of that portion of the solid, or liquid, propellant that is reacting into gases; and the simultaneous release of heat, which causes a high temperature in these gases. It is also interesting to note that with virtually all rocket propellants, as with nitrocellulose, much of the total reaction results from the chemical combination of the two elements that comprise the most plentiful substance on earth, water. Thus, even the reactions taking place in the gigantic rockets that throw vehicles into deep space are essentially those that occur in the small rifles that are used in shooting galleries.

The thermodynamic processes in a rocket motor do not differ essentially from those in a gun. In a rocket, as in a gun, a maximum allowable pressure must not be exceeded. Accordingly, the equation of state dictates a relationship between the allowable quantity and temperature of the gas that can remain in the combustion chamber. This in turn dictates the allowable rate of the reaction. As previously mentioned, one notable difference between a rocket and a gun is that the process in a rocket occurs over a much longer period of time and thus, once the suitable operating pressure is reached, the individual variables in the equation of state, namely pressure, volume, and temperature, remain fairly constant throughout the combustion process. As in a gun, or in any other combustion or energy conversion process, the two laws of thermodynamics must prevail.

The physics of rocket motion is identically related to the motion of a gun. In a gun we are concerned principally with the motion of the projectile and only secondarily with the recoil motion of the gun. In a rocket, on the other hand, we are mainly concerned with the motion of its recoil from firing a multiplicity of gaseous bullets. In any event the total motion of the rocket derives directly from Newton's three laws of motion. In the discussion of Newton's laws in Chapter 4 principal emphasis was placed on the Second Law relating force to motion, and on the Third Law which underlies recoil motion. With a rocket that requires precise adjustment in flight so as to land on, or pass a prechosen distance from, some other planet, there is cause to appreciate Newton's First Law, which states that a body in motion will continue at a constant velocity and in a constant direction until a force is applied to change it.

As discussed in Chapter 5, the three principal interior ballistic problems for gun systems are: to obtain the desired (projectile) velocity level without exceeding a pre-established peak pressure; to obtain the maximum thermodynamic efficiency (i.e., to obtain the optimum projectile velocity for a given propellant charge); and to obtain the desired performance without exceeding a certain recoil energy. To a great extent these three problems are also those of rocket systems. The peak pressure problem is particularly acute in a rocket since the structure itself must be light in order to obtain a suitably high mass ratio, and so the combustion chamber cannot tolerate pressures too much above the 1000 psi or so at which rocket motors normally operate. The second problem, of efficiency, is particularly important with rockets. The ultimate objective in most rocket systems is to obtain a prechosen high velocity level, and this therefore requires that the specific impulse and the mass ratio be high. In order to ensure that the delivered specific impulse is as high as the propellant should give, proper contouring of the combustion chamber and nozzle is necessary, as well as a carefully controlled burning rate. The third problem, of recoil, is somewhat different in a rocket than it is in a gun. If the gun recoil energy is too heavy it can damage a recoil-absorbing device on an artillery piece or cause excessive discomfort to the small arms shooter. In a rocket whose entire motion is a "recoiling" motion, it is not the recoil energy that can be harmful as much as excessive acceleration, which can cause large forces to act either to damage the structure, or if severe enough, can act to crack a solid-propellant grain. Moreover, an excessive acceleration during launch can be harmful to the space traveler. The severity of these problems is greatly exaggerated as rockets get large and complex. For a huge and complex system like the Apollo manned lunar expedition these problems must be resolved to ensure absolute reliability.

In mentioning the Apollo lunar system it is interesting to note that it has surprising similarities to the fictional moon-gun devised by Jules Verne more than a century ago. The Apollo system, weighing more than six million pounds at launch throws, by means of three stages, a 95,000-pound payload into a seven-mile-per-second escape velocity. The bulk of this payload is used for lunar circumnavigation, for landing, and for lunar escape. Only a three-man capsule returns to earth. This capsule has a fourteen-foot diameter and weighs 12,000 pounds. Verne's three-man capsule had a nine-foot diameter and weighed 20,000 pounds. Whereas the moon-gun was 900 feet long and used 400,000 pounds of nitrocellulose, the Apollo system is 363 feet high at launch and uses more than four million pounds of fuel which, in two of the stages, consists of liquid hydrogen and liquid oxygen. A further interesting point of similarity is that Verne's moon-gun was located in Florida.

The voyage of the three lunar astronauts is the result of an enormous technological background and effort that incorporates almost every field of science. The roots of this venture grew from countless sources in many countries. Yet there is a thread of continuity that goes back to another trio, three monks, working independently of each other, from whom man's first true use of chemical energy was made possible.

# SUGGESTIONS FOR FURTHER READING

Those who will wish to pursue the subject of interior ballistics further may do so in any of several directions: as a science, as a sport, or as a hobby. The suggestions for further reading are therefore given in three categories. The first is for the student who wishes to become more knowledgeable in the science of interior ballistics; the second is for the interested hunter or sportsman whose interests are in technical and factual information about shooting, and the third is for the potential hobbyist who will find a great deal of enjoyment from loading his own ammunition.

## A. *Scientific Bibliography*

For anyone wishing to continue the scientific study of interior ballistics, it is first recommended that he extend his knowledge of chemistry, thermodynamics, and physics and that he become proficient in the use of mathematics, the language in which most of the material on this subject is expressed. The following are excellent texts on interior ballistics.

*Internal Ballistics*, F. R. W. Hunt, *et al*. New York: Philosophical Library, 1951.

*Theory of the Interior Ballistics of Guns*, J. Corner. New York: John Wiley & Sons, 1950.

*The Thermodynamics of Firearms*, C. S. Robinson. New York: McGraw-Hill Book Company, 1943.

## B. *Bibliography for the Shooter*

For those interested in the technology and lore of shooting in general, the following represent a small number of the very good books on the subject.

*The Anatomy of Firearms*, L. R. Wallack. New York: Simon and Schuster, 1965.

*Encyclopedia of Firearms,* edited by Harold L. Peterson. New York: E. P. Dutton & Company, 1965.

*Firearms and Ammunition Fact Book*—an excellent summary published by the NRA (National Rifle Association).

*Gun Digest,* edited by John T. Amber, Gun Digest Company (this annual publication always contains excellent articles on ballistics, guns, and hunting by the leading authorities in the United States).

*The Gunner's Bible,* Bill Riviere. Garden City, N.Y.: Doubleday & Company, 1965.

*Guns,* Dudley Pope. New York: Delacorte Press, 1965.

*Complete Book of Rifles and Shotguns,* Jack O'Connor. New York: Outdoor Life—Harper & Row, 1963.

*Shooter's Guide Handbook*—also published by the NRA.

*Small Arms Design and Ballistics,* Vols. I and II, Colonel Townsend Whelen. Small Arms Technical Publishing Company, 1945.

*Winchester—The Gun that Won the West,* Harold F. Williamson. London: Thomas Yoseloff, Ltd.; Cranbury, N.J.: A. S. Barnes & Company (fifth printing), 1965.

*Winchester-Western Ammunition Handbook.* New York: Pocket Books 1964.

In addition, the interested shooter will want to subscribe to one or more of the following magazines, which contain very good articles on guns, hunting, and ballistics by the top experts and are a must for the serious shooter:

*The American Rifleman* (published by the NRA); *Guns and Ammo; Guns Magazine; Gun World; Guns and Game; Gun Week; Gunsport; Guns and Hunting.*

## C. *Reloader's Bibliography*

There are several excellent books on reloading ammunition, of which the following is only a partial list.

*Complete Guide to Handloading,* Philip B. Sharpe. New York: Funk & Wagnalls Company, 1937.

*Handloader's Digest,* edited by John T. Amber. Chicago: Gun Digest Company, 1966.

*Lyman Reloading Handbook*, Ed Matunas. Middlefield, Conn.: The Lyman Gun Sight Corporation, 1967.

*Reloading Handbook*. Washington, D.C.: NRA, 1961.

*Speer's Manual for Reloading Ammunition*. Lewiston, Idaho: Speer, Inc., 1964.

# INDEX

# ANCHOR BOOKS

### CHEMISTRY IN ACTION SERIES

# ANCHOR BOOKS

## SCIENCE STUDY SERIES

# Science Study Series (continued)

# ANCHOR BOOKS

# ANCHOR BOOKS

## NATURAL HISTORY LIBRARY

# ANCHOR BOOKS

## ANTHROPOLOGY AND ARCHAEOLOGY

2a